Mindful Strategie Helping College Students Manage Stress

MW00805776

This practical resource offers a much-needed introduction to the why, what, and how of supporting college students through mindfulness and stress-releasing strategies.

Higher education professionals are in a unique position to support, coach, and teach strategies with students to manage anxiety and emotional distress and improve well-being. Drawing on experience from the disciplines of Mental Health, Counseling, and Student Affairs, the authors provide evidence-based practices and tangible techniques supported by the latest brain-based research and neuroscience. Full of tools that college students can use daily to assist with their relaxation, meditation, focus, and stress management, this book helps higher education professionals who are not trained mental health practitioners to effectively and confidently incorporate activities to support the whole student.

Lacretia Dye is associate professor of Clinical Mental Health Counseling at Western Kentucky University, USA.

Monica Galloway Burke is professor of Student Affairs in Higher Education at Western Kentucky University, USA.

Cynthia Palmer Mason is professor of School Counseling at Western Kentucky University, USA.

Mindful Strategies for Helping College Students Manage Stress

A Guide for Higher Education Professionals

Lacretia Dye,
Monica Galloway Burke,
and Cynthia Palmer Mason

Routledge
Taylor & Francis Group

NEW YORK AND LONDON

First published 2021
by Routledge
52 Vanderbilt Avenue, New York, NY 10017

and by Routledge
2 Park Square, Milton Park, Abingdon, Oxon, OX14 4RN

Routledge is an imprint of the Taylor & Francis Group, an informa business

© 2021 Taylor & Francis

Library of Congress Cataloging-in-Publication Data
Names: Dye, Lacretia, 1975- author. | Burke, Monica Galloway,
author. | Mason, Cynthia Palmer, 1938- author.
Title: Mindful strategies for helping college students manage
stress: a guide for higher education professionals/Lacretia Dye,
Monica Galloway Burke, and Cynthia Mason.
Identifiers: LCCN 2020044659 (print) | LCCN 2020044660 (ebook) |
ISBN 9780367359409 (hardback) | ISBN 9780367359409 (paperback) |
ISBN 9780429342721 (ebook)
Subjects: LCSH: College students–Social conditions. | College students–
Mental health. | Stress management. | Mindfulness (Psychology) |
Counseling in higher education.
Classification: LCC LB3605 .D94 2021 (print) | LCC LB3605 (ebook) |
DDC 378.1/98–dc23
LC record available at https://lccn.loc.gov/2020044659
LC ebook record available at https://lccn.loc.gov/2020044660

ISBN: 978-0-367-35461-9 (hbk)
ISBN: 978-0-367-35940-9 (pbk)
ISBN: 978-0-429-34272-1 (ebk)

Typeset in Perpetua
by Deanta Global Publishing Services, Chennai, India

Contents

Preface   vi

About the Authors   xi

1 Mind, Body, and Spirit: Community Connection and
   Relationships Matter   1

2 Brain Basics   29

3 Relax and Release   50

4 A Meditation a Day   65

5 Mindful Movement   91

6 Helping Students with Focus and Choices for Change   108

7 Self-Care is the New Health Care: Prescriptions for
   Well-Being and Being Well   124

Index   149

Preface

For all of us, there are moments in our lives that we can describe as beautiful and energizing, but we can also point to some moments that are difficult and leave us feeling down and drained. When we encounter these moments that deplete our energy, negatively impact our perceptions and choices, increase our worries, and make us question ourselves, our mind, body, and spirit absorb these thoughts and feelings. Sometimes we may begin to tell ourselves that we are failing and not functioning as well as we really could, getting caught in a feedback loop of negative thoughts and falling victim to them. Sometimes we continue moving forward on autopilot, not taking time to become aware, breathe, reflect, and think about what we need to feel better or heal. What we put our attention to is energizing, and where we put our intention is transforming. Furthermore, since our emotional needs and emotional attachments dictate so much of what we choose to do in life, not having a secure and strong foundation can diminish our ability to be self-confident, trusting, hopeful, and comfortable in the face of conflict. This can also lead to stress and anxiety. In all honesty, stress and anxiety are simply a part of life, but when we have stress and anxiety in our lives, we often feel more pressure because we think everything has to be figured out or healed at that moment. Obviously, we want to feel better sooner, rather than later, but we often do not allow ourselves grace as we move forward toward healing and wellness maintenance. We have to tap into our internal and external resources that are available to us at that point in time and do the best we can to choose what serves us best to heal, grow and move forward. We must ask ourselves: In my daily wellness, am I an active participant or a passive bystander in my healing and growth? We should also acknowledge that there is a difference between recovering and healing. We should then ask ourselves if we can sit with our "selves" to focus on what our mind, body, and spirit need? With the many responsibilities, pursuits, duties, and goals in our lives, it can sometimes become difficult to maintain focus and energy.

Imagine trying to meet the many demands, expectations, and responsibilities of life while transitioning and adapting to a new environment that is intended to build your future and make you a better version of yourself. For many students in higher education, this reality can present challenges for them that bring forth stress and anxiety. In the authors' work with undergraduate and graduate students, over the years, we often encounter moments when we connect with students who feel defeated and worn out from college life. We try to help them through such difficult moments. What we see is that when students are taught to move toward being active participants in their change and growth, they are able to use mindfulness strategies and reflective decision making to reduce their stress and anxiety, thus improving their well-being. Higher education professionals are often on the front line in supporting students who are experiencing mental distress, which can be communicated through conversations with students, students' academic performance, and their behavior on campus. Higher education professionals are in a unique position to support, coach, and teach strategies to students whose stress and anxiety are impacting them in an unproductive way by helping students develop the tools to reduce their stress and anxiety. An added benefit is that students may then feel empowered and self-assured, especially since these strategies and skills can be used in the future.

Human beings and human living are complex. We cannot ignore the idea that all of us are whole beings and our overall health includes our mental states, physical condition, and social environment and that they all influence and connect to each other. In Chapter 1, we focus on the connection of the mind, body, and spirit as well as our connections to our communities and surrounding environments. If we lack in any of these connections, we are affected in ways that can negatively impact our well-being. A sense of social belonging and authentic connections with others and the surrounding environment have been shown to impact the outlook and retention as well as the well-being of college students. Therefore, helping college students find a way to regulate and calm themselves during times of difficulty; connect to others in a healthy, productive way; connect to and engage with their environments; and attend to their dimensions of wellness in nourishing ways can offer benefits that can help them to persist and grow, even beyond college. Group and individual mindful activities that promote community and connection are provided in the chapter.

To understand why stress affects how we think, feel, and act, it is important to understand a little about how the brain works. Our brains are not just a single mass that has one job; the brain is in every cell of the body. Understanding connections in the brain and the connection between the mind and body can help us understand how stress impacts our brains, which in turn affects how we function. In Chapter 2, you will find a description of the brain and brain functions, how brain plasticity can change throughout a person's life, concepts for how the brain is connected to student functioning and stress, and how these brain processes determine our perception of and reactivity to stress. Mindful activities are included that can be used to teach students how the brain works, drawing upon the scholarly work in the fields of biology, neuropsychology, psychology, and counseling.

It is interesting how we can simply think of a regret from the past and then move to a concern for the future, which can bring forth stress and anxiety and take us away from focusing on the present moment. Unfortunately, stress and anxiety can impact so many facets of our lives, specifically our emotional, mental, and physical well-being. In Chapter 3, we focus on the reduction of stress reactions and the activation of relaxation responses that can promote our ability to manage stress, which in turn can mitigate mental and emotional discomfort and distress. For students, mindfulness techniques can serve as a useful tool to reduce stress and increase well-being and productivity. By incorporating mindfulness and meditation into daily routines, students can not only relieve the pressure, but also improve their well-being. This chapter describes the different types of stress, especially the unique stressors of college students, and how stress impacts the body and emotions. Included in the chapter are activities that can be used to teach students how to relax the brain stress response and activate the relaxation response. College life can be stressful, but it should not be overwhelming.

There are several known benefits of incorporating meditation into your life—it reconnects you with what is present and essential in your life experiences; enhances your physical health and mental well-being; relieves your stress; lowers your blood pressure; improves concentration, memory, and learning; and improves sleep and mood. Considering the positive impacts of meditation, students incorporating such healthy practices that relieve stress and improve their relaxation can also help them harmonize their body, mind, and emotions. In Chapter 4, we offer a brief overview of the benefits of meditation, its ability to change brain structure, and the scholarship that supports its use. Included are 31 meditations and/or practices, one for each day, that are specifically created to address the unique stressors of college life.

Mindfulness can include more than sitting still and resting the mind. Mindfully moving can help us be more aware of our body and can be used as a means to decrease stress and anxiety as well as enhance our well-being. Mindful movement—exercise performed with awareness of bodily and emotional responses—can improve a college student's self-regulation and well-being. In Chapter 5, we review mindful movement and the relationship between movement and emotions. In addition, mindful movement practices that can minimize a student's static sedentary life and move them toward one that is more fluid and better for their wellness are provided.

From the day students arrive on campus, they make decisions that shape every aspect of their academic and social lives. Whether choosing a major or to join a Greek-letter organization or to take part in a study abroad opportunity or what to eat for dinner, decision-making becomes a core experience of their college life. Since making choices that, in some cases, can be potentially life framing, a college student being able to use intentional strategies that keep them in the present moment can be beneficial. In Chapter 6, we review choice theory and how higher education professionals can use this paradigm to help college students enhance their focus in their decision-making and how to implement basic principles of the theory to help them bring about change. Used in tandem with mindfulness techniques, these integrated strategies can help students comprehend their responsibility in decision making and the outcomes of their choices, which can enhance their well-being.

Internally, our bodies are constantly functioning and organizing to maintain our health. Learning to maximize this functioning and manage our body's "pharmacy" by optimizing our nutrition, achieving a relaxed mental state and stillness, getting the right physical and mental exercise, getting in touch with nature, and acquiring quality sleep are ideal ways to maintain, regain, and enhance our health. In Chapter 7, we discuss how our bodies can serve as a "pharmacy" for our well-being and how we can write "prescriptions" and plans unique to us for self-care. As self-care is an ideal practice to manage stress and anxiety as well as a way to proactively take care of ourselves, higher education professionals can encourage students to engage in self-care activities and assist them with developing a plan with the activity suggestions, worksheets, and assessment forms included in the chapter.

One way higher education professionals can help students in need with improving their mental and emotional health is through using and teaching students mindfulness and body-based stress-releasing activities as well as reflection and awareness skills when making decisions. These strategies, which can be adapted to fit the unique experiences of college life, can be used by students when faced with stressors. The aim of this book is to offer insights and information about the why, what, and how of using the mind–body–spiritual and community connections, wiring of the brain, decision-making processes for change, and mindfulness and stress releasing activities and strategies to help reduce the stress and anxiety of college students. While the book is written for professionals who are new to mindfulness and mind-body wellness, it can also offer reminders for those with a more advanced awareness.

To provide context for higher education professionals, each chapter includes "Take a Moment" sections, which allow the reader to reflect upon the information shared. These thought-provoking queries, which can be considered individually or with others, can aid the reader in clarifying their approach to using mindfulness strategies with students. "Voices" are also shared in each chapter that offer individuals' insights about mindfulness practice and its basics. In addition to the guidelines and strategies offered for higher education professionals to use with students experiencing stress and anxiety, included in the book are activities, worksheets, assessments, and comments from students and faculty about mindfulness strategies.

Most importantly, the intention of this book is twofold. In an act to support the whole student, the higher education professional brings the same awareness to themselves. The head-to-heart journey of the higher education professional is just as important, if not more important, than their students' journey. You see, as higher education professionals, when we are well, our students are more inclined to be well. As we care for ourselves, we also care for our students. Use this book as a tool to be well and to help your students to be well.

About the Authors

Lacretia Dye is an associate professor of Clinical Mental Health Counseling at Western Kentucky University. As a licensed professional clinical counselor and a national certified counselor, Dr Dye has served her local, regional, and national community with heart, mind, and body wellness for over 20 years. She is trained and certified in a variety of interventions that focus on the integration of counseling, neuroscience, and trauma-informed body-based healing processes. She regularly gives workshops with parents, teachers, students, and community professionals in the areas of ancestral healing, shamanic healing, yoga and drumming therapy, trauma-releasing activities in counseling, urban school counseling, and unconscious bias. She has published and presented at national and international conferences on these topics. A sample of Dr Dye's published articles and monographs includes "A Social Constructivist Approach to Preparing School Counselors to Work in Urban Schools," "Calm, Cool & Confident: Integrating Mindful Yoga into your School Counseling Program," "Group Counseling: African American Adolescent Females' Resiliency, Self-efficacy and Racial Identity," "Beyond Social Justice for the African American Learner: A Contextual Humanistic Perspective," and "Striving to Thrive: Community and Cultural Wealth and Legal Immigration Status." Dr Dye has also conducted over 200 presentations/workshops. Some of these presentations include "Love More Stress Less," "Black Minds Matter," "Black Girl Magic," "Living with Emotions but not Being Your Emotions," "Boy Ninjas, Warriors and Other Big Energies," and "Unconscious Bias in Schools." She is always excited to spend time with session participants.

Monica Galloway Burke is a professor in the Department of Counseling and Student Affairs at Western Kentucky University. Prior to her 22 years of experience as a faculty member and practitioner in Student Affairs and Higher Education, she worked in the field of mental health. Dr Burke has authored numerous peer-reviewed articles in scholarly journals and has contributed chapters to various books. She also served as the lead author for *Helping Skills* *for Working with College Students: Applying Counseling Theory to Student Affairs Practice*; a co-editor for *No Ways Tired: The Journey for Professionals of Color in Student Affairs*, a three-set volume; and a co-editor for *Helping College Students in Distress: A Faculty Guide.* Additionally, she has conducted numerous workshops and presentations at the international, national, regional, state, and local levels. Dr Burke currently serves and has served on editorial boards of professional journals as a co-editor, associate editor, and reviewer. She has also supervised numerous research theses, dissertations, and research projects. Dr Burke has been recognized for her commitment to preparing graduate students for a career in student affairs, her work to promote the field of student affairs and diversity in higher education, her advising and research work, and her collaboration with colleagues and students by receiving various awards from WKU, professional organizations, and the Bowling Green community.

Cynthia Palmer Mason is a professor in the Department of Counseling and Student Affairs at Western Kentucky University. She started her professional career in the Hopkins County School System at Madisonville North Hopkins High School. Her positions in the school system included classroom teacher, secondary school counselor, counseling department chair, advanced placement coordinator, and college board representative. Perhaps her most significant contribution to the school and the community was made possible by the approval of a grant for minority and low-income students that was written by her and her superintendent. For those students, money from this grant covered course fees, books, supplies, tutoring services, dues for organization memberships, and any school-related travel. Through her involvement with these students, she had the opportunity to encourage many of them to attend college, being the first from their families to do so. Since being on the faculty at Western Kentucky University, Dr Mason has been actively involved at the department, college, and university level. She is a Glasser Scholar who completed a 3-year program at the William Glasser Institute that provided Reality Therapy Certification, CT/RT Supervision Certification, and a CT/RT Faculty Endorsement in 2011. Her research interests include the implementation of comprehensive, developmental school counseling programs; the essence of choice theory, reality therapy, and lead management principles in schools; and efforts to decrease the academic achievement gap in P-12 schools. She has authored numerous peer-reviewed articles in scholarly journals; contributed to book reviews and chapters in various books; and presented at the local, state, national, and international levels. Dr Mason has been recognized for her performance in teaching, research, and service by being named a Distinguished Member of WKU's Faculty and Staff in 2009; a "Hats Off to Women Honoree" in 2013; and the recipient of the NAACP's Ambassador of Education Award in 2015.

Chapter 1

Mind, Body, and Spirit

Community Connection and Relationships Matter

If you have ever conversed with a college student about their life or how they are doing, it is likely you have heard comments about how they are dealing with multiple deadlines, stress, anxiety, fatigue, and/or burnout. At its core, college is an environment filled with independence and new opportunities to learn, grow, interact, discover, choose, and evaluate. Unfortunately, during college, students are also vulnerable to a wide range of emotional and mental health challenges that could impact them physically. The college years can be one of the most stressful periods in young adults' lives since they need to manage their own lives (Cress & Lampman, 2007). In addition to dealing with college life, students are also in the midst of emerging adulthood that comprises identity exploration, instability, self-focus, feeling in between taking responsibility for themselves and not completely feeling like an adult, as well as possessing possibilities as well as unparalleled opportunities (Arnett, 2004). While attempting to balance the many responsibilities and expectations of college life as well as their navigation into adulthood, college students are at risk of developing unhealthy behaviors and adverse consequences associated with their mental, emotional, cognitive, spiritual, and physical well-being at the micro (e.g., student and their performance in the classroom) and macro (e.g., academic, residential, and social) level of the campus community. Such experiences and emotions can impact a variety of aspects of a college student's life, which underscores the need for them to learn strategies to help them through life's difficult moments.

Considering the scope and importance of the personal well-being of college students, higher education professionals have a distinctive opportunity to support and advocate for the mental and emotional and health of students, especially at a particularly vulnerable point in students' lives. In addition, higher education professionals are in a unique position to understand and support students' psychological and social resources, which can amend their experiences with overwhelming stress. Psychological resources (e.g., an individual's attitudes and dispositions) are what we are taught and what is modeled for us by mature adults in our lives.

These resources are our perspectives—such as hope, patience, and encouragement—and the skills we learn—such as relaxation, mindfulness, asking for help, and tolerating anxiety (Burke, Laves, Sauerheber, & Hughey, 2020). Social resources are, essentially, the people with whom we have relationships or can be found in the groups we belong to or are affiliated with at the time. Having a support system (e.g., family, friends, and acquaintances) and the relationship skills to find and maintain relationships with these supportive people can also help buffer the effects of stress (Burke, Laves, Sauerheber, & Hughey, 2020). Higher education professionals can aid students by working with them to help mitigate their stress and by securing resources to offer appropriate support in order to help students cope with stress.

Understanding the connection between the mind, body, and spirit and the relevance of our connection to others is a first step toward helping students, through the use of mindful strategies, manage stress. We simply cannot ignore the idea that as humans, we are whole beings, that our overall health includes our mental states, physical condition, and social environment, and that they all influence each other.

A STUDENT'S VOICE

While in college, I wish I would have learned how to better put time aside for my mental health. To this day, I find myself putting all of my energy into work and academics until I "crash." Self-care is something I wish could have been better talked about by not only schools, but also parents, professionals and counselors while I attended undergrad.

—A 24-year-old graduate student

MENTAL HEALTH AND THE COLLEGE STUDENT

Our mental health, a state of well-being in which an individual can cope with the normal stresses of life, work productively and fruitfully, and is able to make a contribution to their community (World Health Organization, 2018), includes our emotional, psychological, and social well-being and determines how we handle stress, relate to others, and make choices. When our mental health is in a good state, we manage our basic cognitive and social skills;

recognize, express, and modulate our emotions; are flexible and able to cope with adverse life events; function in social roles; and modulate a harmonious relationship between our body and mind (Galderisi et al., 2015). Of course, as we grow in life, we are at times presented with obstacles and circumstances, seen and unforeseen, which can negatively impact the state of our mental health, bringing forth emotions such as anxiety, fear, worry, frustration, disappointment, sadness, and anger. Specifically, an unforeseen circumstance such as the coronavirus 2019 (COVID-19) pandemic, which impacted the academic and environmental realms on many college campuses in the United States, accentuates how an unexpected event can cause psychological stress, put students' coping strategies to the test, and may lead to unfavorable effects on their academic performance. The unexpected changes to learning formats, living situations, proximity to peers, relationships with friends and partners, extracurricular activities, work and finances, routines, the job market, and academic celebrations triggered anxiety and stress for some students. These changes occurred in addition to concerns regarding infection and transmission of COVID-19 to others. A consequence of increased stress and anxiety due to unexpected changes such as a pandemic can lead to mind wandering, which then competes for limited cognitive resources; this has a number of real-world consequences, such as effects on academic performance and the ability to complete daily tasks (Boals & Banks, 2020). Additionally, the national protests for racial equality and justice in the United States also presented unique challenges for the campus and students, particularly the mental health of Black students. Seeing and hearing disparaging comments about a dimension of who you are, from which you cannot hide, in media and on campus can have a detrimental impact on the psychological well-being of students of color. Currie and colleagues (2012) found that the most common psychological reaction for students experiencing discrimination was to feel a sense of helplessness and hopelessness. Racial battle fatigue (RBF) has also been used to describe such experiences of students of color in postsecondary settings, which affirms that the cumulative, negative effect of racial microaggressions causes them to often become physically and emotionally drained (Smith, 2009). Therefore, when uncertainties enter the lives of college students and they are not able to effectively stay well in their mind, body, and spirit, they can face mental health challenges.

Particularly, there has been more attention on the mental and emotional well-being of adolescents and emerging adults, especially the stress and anxiety of college students, over the past few years. Today's college students continue to suffer at least as much as previous generations and may be less able to function as self-assured and autonomous individuals (Burke, Sauerheber, Hughey & Laves,

2017). In fact, studies have shown that common mental health issues reported by American college students include depression, stress, anxiety, and suicidal ideation in addition to concerns about feeling lonely and overwhelmed, relationships, family, and interpersonal functioning (American College Health Association, 2018; Brandy, Penckofer, Solari-Twadell, & Velsor-Friedrich, 2015; LeViness, Bershad, & Gorman, 2017). In spring 2018, for example, the National College Health Assessment (American College Health Association, 2018) reported that more than half of students (57.6%) reported they had experienced more than average or tremendous stress and overwhelming anxiety (63.4%) within the last 12 months.

Considering the increased likelihood that college students will experience stress and anxiety during their college journey, higher education professionals can prepare themselves to play a role in supporting students during mental health challenges due to life events such as relationships, finances, academic pressures, and concerns about their future career. As recommended by Kitzrow (2003), student mental health should be perceived as an important, legitimate concern and the responsibility of everyone in the campus community, including administrators, faculty, and staff, rather than being the sole responsibility of the counseling center and of particular concern to student affairs staff who work closely with students. Higher education professionals can learn and use strategies, such as mindfulness strategies, to help students get well and stay well. A first step to understanding how mindfulness strategies can be used to help students with stress and anxiety is to foster an understanding about how the mind, body, spirit, community connection, and environment can affect thinking, emotional well-being, physical well-being, and socialization.

THE MIND

Defining the mind can be an interesting task, especially when you consider its complexity. The complexity is derived from several concepts associated with the mind, such as the core of human consciousness and awareness, the source for the connection of thinking and feeling, the foundation for the flow of information, the residence of our faculties, and the source of mental stability and balance. The mind is also the place where we can breed and feed our insecurities, pain, and internal battles. As such, the mind has been referred to as both healer and slayer, since our thoughts, feelings, and perceptions impact our health and longevity (Freeman, 2009). Let's face it; our mind can be our biggest ally or our worst enemy. As Siegel (2020) asserted, "The mind is an embodied and relational process that regulates the flow of energy and information" (p. 5). Considering the power of the mind, it would befit us to identify ways in which our mind can move

4

us forward or hold us back, and how the regulation of our flow of energy and information influences our emotional state.

What is powerful about the mind is that it influences how we perceive our experiences, and our experiences impact how we perceive reality and develop a worldview. It is a simple thought, but a complex process. Let's say that a person consistently lets negative thoughts about them and their life, at the conscious and unconscious levels, flow through their mind. Such thoughts can impact their feelings, relationships, performance, and accomplishment of life goals. With this repetitiveness of negative thoughts, they can begin to feel trapped in their circumstances and unable to see a way out. However, if they become so uncomfortable to the point that they want to enhance their well-being by making a personal change, which is an intentional act, they will have to evolve their brain (in essence, change their mind) by using its natural capacity of neuroplasticity (the ability to rewire and create new neural circuits) (Dispenza, 2007). This process can be possible because the mind is not simply brain activity; it is also a self-organizing, emergent process of a complex system that is within us and functions between us and others (Siegel, 2020). To gain awareness and modify that awareness to accomplish a desired change, which can be a difficult process, we must first have some understanding of how our mental processes function within the brain (discussed in Chapter 2). In the end, we must remember that we are asking a lot of ourselves when we decide to make a significant change and self-regulate; therefore, patience and grace must not be in short supply.

TAKE A MOMENT

Take a brief moment and ask yourself or others the following questions.

- How do I eliminate negative thoughts and investigate my being (including my attitudes, beliefs, and patterns/habits)?
- In what way do I notice how my actions are serving me?
- How do I reconcile my experiences and reframe the dynamics in my life?
- How do I facilitate the release of negative patterns from my mind?
- What have I learned from my experiences to frame my mindset?
- How can I be more compassionate and patient with myself?

A STUDENT'S VOICE

College life personally and academically is stressful and can definitely make you feel drained, overwhelmed, and create anxiety if I was having difficulty creating a balance in my life. The whole experience of sitting down in my chair in a low lit room with meditative music, sometimes silence, or the strike of an alpha and theta wave chime helped calm me down and enabled me to think clearly. I was able to move racing thoughts that caused me difficulties concentrating and had an overall better state of mind moving to other classes or academic work I had to accomplish. To be still and in the present moment listening to the mind and really paying attention to the body is an experience like no other. It definitely helped make me a better student, but more than that, it gave me a tool to utilize that I can carry for the rest of my life.

—An undergraduate student

THE MIND AND BODY

A biochemical link exists between the mind and the body, and since the body and mind are indistinguishably connected, each time we have a thought, we set off a movement of cellular reactions in our nervous system that influences all the molecules in our body (Pert, 1997). Our state of being consists of a repetitive cycle of our thoughts and feelings combined with the production of chemicals within our body, which generates our emotions. With every thought we have, there is a surge of electrical currents from our brain that releases an unknown number of neurochemicals, and our body responds to each thought accordingly (Dispenza, 2007). In essence, we have to be mindful of our thoughts. Any repetitive feeling (e.g., happiness, sadness, loneliness, and insecurity) can create a feedback loop between the brain and the body (Dispenza, 2007). For example, you feel lonely and think about your loneliness, which can breed worry about being alone for the rest of your life, which in turn makes you anxious, which then makes you feel more worried, and on and on this process goes. Thus, our mind, which includes our mental states such as thoughts, emotions, beliefs, attitudes, and perceptions, can positively or negatively affect how our bodies function.

An example of this mind–body connection is how your body responds to stress and worry. Imagine a time you felt a tremendous amount of stress or anxiety. Perhaps you had to conduct a presentation or speech to influence others, be somewhere important on time but encountered unexpected delays, or wait for an important test result. Can you remember how you felt? Did you experience uneasiness, racing or unwanted thoughts, or fear? Did you experience an increased pulse rate, altered breathing, sweaty palms, or tightness in your body such as your neck, jaw, muscles, or stomach? Did you experience difficulty concentrating or making decisions, forgetfulness, procrastination, inefficiency, or mood swings? When stress and anxiety appear, our bodies will often react. Constant worry and stress over life circumstances and problems can cause muscle tenseness, headaches, and stomach problems as well as lead to high blood pressure or other health problems. As described by Dispenza (2007), "the chemicals of stress are the culprits that begin to alter our internal state and pull the trigger of cellular breakdown" (p. 8). So when we feel physical or psychological stress, the fight or flight response is triggered automatically (e.g., your heart beats faster and your muscles tense up), which is the result of the release of stress hormones in the body, such as cortisol and adrenaline. Conspicuously, perceived stress can have implications for our health, which is another reason we must remain observant of the mind–body connection.

In addition, the mind and body communicate messages to each other resulting in biochemical and physiological changes, which can modulate whether our body is likely to support health or disease (Freeman, 2009). Conversely, what we do with our physical body (e.g., our diet and nutrition, physical activity, and posture) can impact our mental state. We can connect the dots about how communication between our mind and body can impact our wellness. Attending to our wellness involves finding time to be quiet, silence stressful thoughts, and alleviate tensions in the body.

The mind–body connection is basically embedded in our human existence. As we move toward mindfulness, emotional regulation, and managing stress, we must recognize this connection and how it presents in our lives. As we are more than our minds and our bodies, we must also consider the connection of the two to our spirit.

TAKE A MOMENT

Take a brief moment and ask yourself or others the following questions.

- How does my body inform me that I need a release?
- How do I interpret the connection of my mind, body, and spirit?
- How do I notice the feedback loop I am experiencing?
- How do I let my body inform me of what I need?

THE MIND, BODY, AND SPIRIT

Beyond the physical and mental dimensions in our lives, there is also a spiritual dimension to our human experience. Spirituality is defined in various ways, including as an existential reality, connectedness, and energy (Chiu et al., 2004), or as a dimension concerned with the transcendent and the meaning of life (Hiatt, 1986; Young & Koopsen, 2005). Spirituality is individualistic, emotionally oriented, inwardly directed, and unifying, without formal rules and doctrines (Koenig, McCullough, & Larson, 2000). Dyer (2004) noted that the way we establish a relationship with our spirit is by continuously contemplating ourselves and being surrounded by the conditions we wish to produce. Aptly, a person's spiritual path depends on their ability to increase their awareness of what is happening internally as well as externally in their lives. Therefore, what a person chooses to surround themselves with is important to raise their awareness. Doing so can help with identifying a sense of purpose and meaning in life.

The mind, the body, and the spirit do not operate in isolation, and all three are components of our individual wellness. The mind, body, and spirit are interconnected and interact in dynamic ways with one another (Young & Koopsen, 2005), and when the mind, body, and spirit are acknowledged and connected, we can be more regulated. Therefore, if the body is not well and needs care, the mind and spirit do too, and if the mind is filled with anxiety and stress, the body and spirit can react. Understanding our natural states and how they produce and facilitate a healthy state of being are key in maintaining a balance in our mind–body–spirit connection. When and if things become unbalanced, becoming aware of how our mental thoughts shape and influence our physical and emotional state is an important first step, especially since interactions occur among our thoughts, our body, and our external world. Focusing on the mind–body–spirit connection acknowledges the power of the mind and body as well as the fundamental meaning of spirituality and human existence, which extends to an individual's broader perception of self that connects them to a larger sense of themselves and their communities.

In higher education, where the focus is mostly on student learning and growth in and out of the classroom, what cannot be ignored is the relevance of connections for students—the connection of the mind, body, and spirit as well as the connection to others and the environment. As students journey through their day to meet their responsibilities and demands, it may become necessary for them to become aware and balance their mind, body, and spirit in a way that will support good thoughts, good health, and well-being. One way to increase awareness is to integrate mindful activities into our lives so the physical body can communicate with our mental and spiritual selves (Kabat-Zinn, 1991; Solloway, 2000). Teaching students about essential strategies that can help with increasing their awareness and aligning their mind, body, and spirit can serve as a measure of support as they matriculate.

8

TAKE A MOMENT

Take a brief moment and ask yourself or others the following questions.

- How do I facilitate the release of negative patterns in my mind, body, and spirit?
- How do I remove the "junk" in my mind, body, and spirit to get to reconciliation and peace?
- What tools do I use to overcome feeling "out of sync" with my natural state?
- What is my spiritual goal?
- How do I protect my space and peace?
- How do I get to my authentic self?

CONNECTING TO THE COMMUNITY AND SOCIAL BELONGING

Having a connection to another person is a common human want and need. In point of fact, human connection has always been necessary for the survival of the species, and as we now live in a modern time where it is possible to isolate ourselves almost entirely in our homes, our mental health can suffer as a result because of a lack of connection. Our mental, emotional, and social well-being are naturally nurtured through making and maintaining human connections. According to the "belongingness hypothesis" (Baumeister & Leary, 1995), humans possess a pervasive nature to form and maintain strong, stable, and nonaversive interpersonal relationships and attachments within an ongoing relational bond, and a lack of belongingness could have a harmful effect on both short- and long-term health and well-being, including emotional health and cognitive processes. For example, the lockdown and social distancing associated with the pandemic in 2020 may have been an impetus for some individuals to experience loneliness and disregard the mandates, which can occupy the mind, body, and spirit.

In the bigger scheme of things, we are wired to be social, stay connected, and have a purpose. There is a viewpoint that the human brain cannot sustain purposeless living because it was naturally designed to facilitate meaningful thought and action (Klinger, 1998), and personal relationships make up a central meaning in human life (Klinger, 1977). Thus, feeling a sense of connection to others contributes to our sense of purpose and meaning making (Steger, 2012; Steger, Oishi, & Kashdan, 2009). Having a sense of purpose through our connections with others can also provide us with a feeling of significance and reinforcement of our true, authentic selves. There tends to be a pleasant and comforting feeling in many of us when we are hugged, actively listened to, emotionally understood, and supported by another person. The structure of a community could cultivate an individual's ability to give and receive support as well as have access to concern, nurturing, healthy communication, and other desirable resources related to connection.

Having a sense of belonging to a community is also an important factor in a person's life. Knowing that one's needs are being met and the community is a safe place that adds to sense of well-being may add more meaning to an individual's life (Lambert et al., 2013). A sense of belonging to a community also enhances the feelings and perceptions a person has about their environments (Balaswamy & Richardson, 2001). Social belonging and connectedness are also related to many positive emotions, such as feeling accepted, included, or welcomed, which leads to positive feelings such as happiness and satisfaction; however, negative emotions—such as being refused, excluded, or ignored—might result in negative feelings such as anxiety, depression, and loneliness (Baumeister & Leary, 1995). Of course, most of us would prefer not to experience the painful feelings associated with social loss and rejection, especially when we lose valued connections. In essence, a sense of community and a connection to others are strongly related to an individual's well-being.

Life affords many wonderfully meaningful moments and can be profound in many ways through our connections with others (e.g., friendships, close and caring family, and romantic relationships). When there is a discrepancy between our desire for connection to other people and the actual connection that we have, feelings of loneliness can occur (Christakis & Fowler, 2009). Loneliness (i.e., feeling alone) and social isolation (i.e., being alone), actual and perceived, can be harmful to physical and mental health (Holt-Lunstad et al., 2015). On the other hand, we all want to flourish, be content, and feel supported and connected with others; but when we experience a diminished mental capacity—cognitive, emotional, attentional, interpersonal, motivational, or behavioral—our enjoyment of life or interactions with society and the surrounding environment can be adversely affected (Stephens, Dulberg, & Joubert, 1999). In the end, we want to feel included and feel like we are a valued part of a community. Social support benefits individuals' well-being and sustains their sense of mattering, self-esteem, and belonging, which in turn should mitigate stress, distress, and physiological arousal (Thoits 2011). Oftentimes, when we connect, contribute to a cause or someone in need, and do good, we feel good.

Social connectedness, a sense of belonging, and a sense of community are associated with the psychosocial and academic adjustment of college students (Ostrove & Long, 2007). As Molasso (2006) reported, activities that engage students with others within the campus community are positively related to their development of purpose. Psychological feelings of fitting in, acceptance, and support from a group or community are important elements of retention and the student's perception of the institution (Strayhorn, 2012). Therefore, it is necessary to acknowledge the role of a connection between the campus community and the college students as well as how the disconnection of the mind, body, and spirit and the environment can be harmful or stressful and may contribute to various levels of distress.

TAKE A MOMENT

Take a brief moment and ask yourself or others the following questions.

- How do I create a sense of space where I belong?
- What value do I find in the communities to which I belong?
- How do I protect my energy when I am around others who tend to deplete it?
- What strategies do I use to ensure that there is time in the day to interact with my community?
- How do I communicate my expectations and needs to my community/ communities?
- Has lacking a sense of belonging affected how I feel about myself?
- Has lacking a community to which I feel that I belong caused me to make sacrifices in terms of my well-being and/or sense of self?
- Given my talents, passions, and values, how can I serve, help, or contribute?

Connection to the Environment

Just as whoever is around us affects our emotions and energy, so can what is around us. Have you ever been in a space where you found it difficult to accomplish your tasks or focus because of uncleanliness, clutter, noisiness, unpleasant smells, or dimness? When things around you are cluttered or distracting, your mind can also be cluttered and distracted. Each of us is influenced by the living and nonliving aspects of our environment. Social environments, which consist of social entities (e.g., living and nonliving as well as human and nonhuman) and the complex networks that connect these entities, also impact well-being. For example, college students can be impacted by the living (e.g., peers, professors, staff, nature) and the nonliving (e.g., academic buildings, walkways, residence halls) aspects of a college community.

Nonliving entities and aesthetics can influence our energy and mood. Aesthetics involves a focus on aspects of an object under our consideration that is subjectively perceived as pleasing to our senses and/or our cognitive capacities that elicits emotions (Menninghaus et al., 2019). For example, living spaces, which include the buildings, landscape, and aesthetics of a college campus, can all be considered as influencers to connection and community. Just as a formal meditation practice can calm us, connect us to self, and soothe our nervous systems in a nourishing way, so too can the spaces where we live, eat, sleep, and traverse. Nonliving aesthetics, such as light, smell, colors, furniture, and space layout, can play a role in how we connect to our surrounding environment.

Light

Light is essential for our health and well-being. Light directly impacts mood and learning/cognition, brought about by two different and distinct pathways from the retina into the brain (Fernandez et al., 2018). A lack of natural light is also linked to depressive symptoms and cognitive dysfunction. Intrinsically photosensitive retinal ganglion cells (ipRGCs) target many visual centers in the brain, including the circadian pacemaker and the area responsible for pupil constriction, among many others, and are critical for the influence of light on circadian rhythms, sleep, mood, and pupil constriction (Berson, Dunn, & Takao, 2002; Hatter et al., 2002). The 24-hour cycle, circadian rhythm, is very responsive to the presence of light and shaped by changes in the external environment (e.g., changing levels of daylight). Ensuring that we receive adequate levels of light can benefit our mood, alertness, productivity, sleep pattern, and other aspects of our functioning. Increasing our exposure to sunlight can heighten the brain's production of the mood-enhancing chemical serotonin. Sunshine absorbed through the skin may directly stimulate the production of serotonin (Sansone & Sansone, 2013), a chemical that is considered a natural mood stabilizer and is sometimes referred to as the happy chemical. If you can, try to fit natural light into your busy schedule by taking a walk. Going outside and taking in the sun could give you energy as well as help your mental and physical well-being. Open the blinds and curtains and allow the sun to shine through the windows. These suggestions are especially true for college students who spend a lot of time tapping away at a computer, studying, and engaging with their phone. Doing so can help them to destress and be mindful.

In addition, Knez and Kers (2000) have indicated that indoor lighting also directly affects our emotions, memory, perceptual orientation, and problem-solving abilities. Since the use of electric light began, a blurring of the boundaries of day and night has made it more difficult to synchronize biological processes (Bedrosian & Nelson, 2017), which affects sleep and health. As we tend to spend more time inside, we must pay attention to how we use light in our inside spaces. The tone or color of the light is also relevant; therefore, the use of brighter lights is suggested during the day, while dimmer lights are recommended for night. Warm lights (yellowish color light) make the environment feel quieter and more relaxing, while cooler lights (whitish color light) make the environment more stimulating. There is also blue light (like daylight light bulbs), which is purported to reduce levels of melatonin (the sleep-related hormone) that can make us feel more awake. We should try to avoid the use of cold (luminescence) or blue light at bedtime to improve our quality of sleep and positively affect our mood and well-being. Although it is not possible to control the lighting in all the environments and spaces we occupy, we can be aware of the impact lighting has on our mood and body and modify accordingly when we can. This realization is especially true for college students when they are in most areas of campus, but when studying and sleeping in their room, awareness about lighting could be helpful.

Color

Colors, based on our perceptions, can impact emotions and behaviors. Think about the colors we wear or choose to buy, which could reflect how we are feeling or how we want others to perceive us. As Kingston (2016) recommends, you should not go shopping when you feel emotionally "out of sorts" because the colors in your energy field could be impacted (and the colors that look great to you then might not the next day, once that emotion has dissipated). Different colors are presumed to have different associations, and viewing a color is thought to trigger psychological responses consistent with these associations (Elliot & Maier, 2007). For example, the colors of the food on our plate can make it look appealing, but on the other hand, we will frown upon the plate if we associate the colors with things that we consider unpleasant. Stone (2003) asserted that warm colors (e.g., red and orange) help us focus outwards and increase our awareness, whereas cool colors (e.g., blue and green) turn us inward and help us focus on visual and mental tasks. Warm colors stimulate feelings, and cool colors are calming colors (Stone & English, 1998). When you walk outside in the spring season and see the fresh blooms spanning the spectrum of colors, how do you feel? What about the warm colors of the fall season? Color can communicate with us as well as stimulate a reaction in us.

Plants

Beyond their aesthetic purpose, plants in your space are good for your health as they release oxygen and absorb carbon dioxide (NASA, n.d.). This process not only freshens up the air, but also eliminates harmful toxins. Seeing greenery, including in nature, can help us to feel calmer and more relaxed, which in turn benefits our mood. Interacting with indoor plants produces positive feelings and has positive physiological effects on the autonomic nervous system (Lee et al., 2015). In addition, caring for a living thing can give us a purpose and a rewarding feeling, especially if it blooms and thrives.

Furniture and Space Layout

The space in which you are functioning can also affect your mood. Environmental factors (e.g., color, furniture layouts, materials, temperature, and smell) can affect our perceptions, behavioral actions, spatial orientation, and wayfinding (i.e., spatial problem solving) (Hidayetoglu, Yildirim, & Akalin, 2012). Particularly, decluttering your space can improve your mood and improve your focus. Clutter of any kind in your space can create an obstacle to the flow of energy, and cleaning the space clears the stagnant energy that accumulates around clutter (Kingston, 2016). Clutter and unfinished projects can cause anxiousness and stress and serve as reminders that we have unfinished tasks, which are not conducive to one's well-being. In addition, the way you arrange your furniture can also influence whether the space feels functional and harmonious. Feng shui, the art of balancing and harmonizing the flow of natural energy in our surroundings, can have beneficial effects (Kingston, 2016). Additionally, the layout, color, and fabric of furniture in your space can impact your mood. Furthermore, smell chemically connects our brains to our environment, and therefore aromatherapy, the use of plant-based essential oils and hydrosols can help to balance the mind, body, and spirit (Cristina, 2004). For example, inhaling a mixture of peppermint, basil, and helichrysum essential oils several times a day was found to reduce the symptoms of moderate mental exhaustion and/or burnout (Varney & Buckle, 2013). Thus, if you want to positively affect your mood, maybe make small changes to your space's layout, colors, furniture, room scent, and fabrics.

NON-LIVING AESTHETICS & MOOD REGULATION

① LIGHT

Are you being exposed to enough natural light? Natural light can impact your circadian rhythm (or body clock), which can influence sleep patterns, mood, and productivity. Open your blinds and let in some good natural light or take a walk in the sunshine. Use brighter lights during the day and dimmer lights at night.

② PLANTS

Plants release oxygen and absorb carbon dioxide, which freshens up the air and rid it of toxins. Indoor plants can reduce anxiety and stress levels, essentially stimulating a positive mood, and spruce up air quality. Put a plant in your space and take in its benefits.

③ COLOR

Colors change levels of alertness and energy as well as influence moods and mental clarity. The way different colors can affect emotions depends largely on a color's brightness, saturation, shade, tint or tone and the person's perception of the color. For example, red, orange and yellow are warm colors often evoke feelings of happiness, positivity, and energy and cool colors, such as blue and green, are usually calming and soothing. Incorporate colors in your space via art, furniture, or walls.

④ SHAPES

The different characteristics of a shape convey different moods and meanings. Circles represent completion, wholeness and harmony; squares represent order; and rectangles are associated with security, reliability and strength. Shapes can be included in artwork, wall hangings, or fabric.

⑤ PAINTINGS

Paintings are open for interpretation and symbolism and depending on one's perception of the painting will determine if it has a positive or negative influence on mood. The colors in the painting will also affect mood regulation. Select paintings that evoke a positive feeling for your space.

⑥ FURNITURE

Arrangement and shape of the furniture can create harmony in your room and/or home. Arrangement of the furniture can also create a change of energy and flow of the environment.

TAKE A MOMENT

Take a brief moment and ask yourself or others the following questions.

- How are the spaces in which I function working for me?
- What colors make me feel inspired?
- What should I declutter in my life?

DOMAINS OF STUDENT WELL-BEING

There are numerous paradigms focused on our balanced health and lifestyle with distinguishing domains that are based on our capacity to function (e.g., Hettler, 1984; Maslow, 1943; Siegel, 2012; Witmer & Sweeney, 1992). Within this context, five domains are fairly consistent within the various models—body, mind, spirit, relationships/connections, and safety in our environment. While all these domains need our attention, the goal is to find the personal balance of the domains that is most realistic and genuine for us. Of course, to get to the point where all domains are integrated in a way that works best for us, it requires awareness and commitment through the choices we make (Hettler, 1984). Obviously, when helping others, we cannot make choices for them about their health and well-being. As noted by Glasser (2000), all behavior is purposeful, and our choices are our best attempt, given the resources at our disposal at that time, to meet our needs (discussed in Chapter 6). However, what higher education professionals can do is present strategies to students that can help them maneuver through times of high anxiety and stress using the tools they have at their disposal. The chart below, *Domains for Health and Connection*, provides context about five domains, the associated elements, and potential strategies on which to focus when helping others.

DOMAINS FOR HEALTH AND CONNECTION

	DOMAIN	DOMAIN ELEMENTS	STRATEGIES
	My Mind	Logic, reasoning, and intuition	Mindfulness exercises
	How I think,	Mental agility and awareness	Meditation
	reason, analyze,	Motivation	Affirmations
	feel, and perceive	Vision and focus	Self-regulation
		Capabilities and skills	Metacognitive awareness
		Thoughts, feelings/emotions,	Relaxation techniques
		and behavior	Movement interventions
		Self-concept and self-efficacy	Mental
		Self-control	health therapy/counseling
			Work-life integration

(Continued)

Continued

DOMAIN	DOMAIN ELEMENTS	STRATEGIES
My Body How well my body functions and I maintain or strengthen my physical self	Physical health and well-being Genetics Facilitation of energy Conscious movement and involuntary actions	Exercise and activity Diet and nutrition Sleep Hydration Routine medical exams and screenings Safety precautions Body scan meditation Breathwork Mindful movement Posture and ergonomics
My Spirit How I perceive meaning and purpose in my life	System of beliefs, values, and principles Self-authorship and meaning making	Self-reflection Prayer Meditation Journaling Altruism Conscious acts of kindness Gratitude journal Active mindfulness Therapy/counseling
My Connections How I interact and connect with others	Social relationships Support system Social networks Mattering and social belonging	Build social networks Communicate with support system Monitor social media engagement and use Volunteerism Maintenance of relationship boundaries
My Environment How I interact with the environment and how the environment impacts me	Interaction with others Proximity to resources Living conditions Quality of air and water Social environment Feeling safe Connection to nature Aesthetics	Environmental stewardship Fellowship with others Declutter spaces Mindful walk Listen to nature sounds

17

One of the major purposes of American higher education is to develop the student as a whole person and enhance student well-being, which extends beyond student learning and skills attainment to include other pertinent aspects related to growth such as connecting, thinking, feeling, spirituality, and expression. Encouraging students to move toward a holistic integration of the physical, mental, and spiritual domains in their lives as well as making connections to their environment and others can help them gain greater awareness and strive for the life that feels most authentic to them. An emotionally and physically healthy student who feels a sense of belonging and purpose as well as feeling safe will more than likely possess the tools needed to better thrive in college and beyond. Higher education professionals can help students learn strategies they need to enhance their connections and work through stressful life encounters. The following section provides details about mindfulness and mindful activities, including each activity's intention, that can be put into practice to help students, individually or as a group, reduce stress and become more aware.

A STUDENT'S VOICE

Starting class with mindfulness and meditation was completely new to me and I did feel uncomfortable at first because I struggled with sitting in silence and controlling/focusing my thoughts, especially after a long day. Needless to say, starting class that way calmed me down, gave me a chance to breathe, and allowed me to be present in the moment. Because of starting meditation in class, I now meditate in my personal life and love it!

—An undergraduate student

MINDFULNESS STRATEGIES

Mindfulness is a process of being fully present in the moment, suspended from judgment or correction and starting with a simple awareness of one's body and thoughts (Kabat-Zinn, 2003). Existing in an automatic, nonmindful mode can cause an individual to refuse to acknowledge or attend to a thought, emotion, motive, or object of perception and disengage from automatic thoughts, habits, and unhealthy behavior patterns (Brown & Ryan, 2003). Cultivating mindfulness can occur through formal (e.g., yoga and meditation) or informal practice (e.g., noticing the sounds of water and the scent of the soap during a shower).

A range of psychological and physical health benefits are associated with mindfulness interventions (Mehranfar, Younesi, & Banihashem, 2012). Particularly, mindfulness skills have been shown to be effective in increasing relaxation and coping skills when faced with stressful situations (McKay, Wood, & Brantley, 2007). Mindfulness practice gently counters the mind's inherent need to evaluate experiences as positive or negative. Cashwell, Bentley, and Bigbee (2007) also suggested that mindfulness practice may be beneficial for enhancing an individual's capacity for attention and concentration, strengthening their ability to accept the present moment, facilitating greater self-awareness and compassion, and increasing their capacity for self-regulation. The goals of the mindful activities outlined below, focusing on connections and community for an individual or group, are to promote the moving of our bodies together, which primes the brain for learning, shifts emotional states, develops concentration, and releases energy.

CONNECTION ACTIVITIES: PRACTICE AND INTENTION

Community Compliments

Intention: Practice giving and receiving compliments. Provide closure to class/group with a compliment as a special gift from each student.

- Students will write one compliment to each student in the group/class.
- Facilitator/instructor reviews the parts of a VIP compliment (Is it true? Is it kind? Is it specific? Can I articulate a strength? Can I elaborate with example or reason?).
- Give students 2–3 minutes to look around the room and brainstorm general ideas of what they will write during this activity.
- Provide a sheet of paper (place the paper on their desk) or ask each student to provide a sheet of paper. Have them write their name at the top.
- Instructor will invite students to stand and rotate to the left, one desk at a time, to write a compliment on each person's paper.
- Give 45–60 seconds (depending on how many students in class/group) to write one VIP compliment for each person.
- Rotate to the left until the students are back at their desk with their own Compliment Sheet.

Connection Circle

Intention: Community and connection.

Facilitator prep: Make your own Connection Ball by writing questions on a beach ball, or you can purchase "Thumballs" online with questions already on the balls.

- Students stand in a circle.
- Give the Connection Ball to one student.
- When a student has the ball, they say their own name and answer the questions their thumb is on.
- The student with the ball then points to a person across from them, says that person's name, and tosses the ball underhand to them.
- Once a student has caught the Connection Ball, they will put their hands behind their back, so people know not to throw to them again.
- Repeat the process for each student.
- The game continues until everyone has had a chance to answer one Connection question.

Handshakes

Intention: Creatively connecting with others.

- Invite students to get into groups of two or three.
- Students will create a handshake together and memorize it.
- After every pair/triad has created their handshake, then each partner will find another pair to teach their handshake to.
- Another option is to have group vote for a community handshake.

Intuitive Count

Intention: Practice mindfulness and connection.

- Students stand (or sit) in a circle.
- Students close their eyes and sit quietly for a few seconds. Individually, they must each say a number, one at a time. The count is not based on their physical position but based on when they "sense" it is time to speak. Note that they are not speaking in a particular order. They are to count to the number of students participating (i.e., 25 students would count to 25) without saying a number at the same time.

- Each student can only say one number, but the count-off is random and the goal is that they sense a good time to speak.
- When more than one student says the same number at once, they must start again.
- Celebrate small successes and encourage students to connect, pause, and notice before speaking.

Kind Connection Challenge

Intention: Practice kindness.

Students participate in a Kindness Challenge for 48–72 hours. They will practice kindness by doing the following each day:

- Make someone's day by doing one conscious act of kindness (e.g., bake a friend their favorite dessert, compliment three people, ask someone you have never talked to if they would like to join you to eat lunch at your table, create a video of appreciation for someone you care about).
- Do one "that's not my job" job—something that you do not have to do for someone (e.g., household chore, offering to help pick up trays at lunch, pick up litter on a street).
- Encourage students to do these acts without people knowing it was them.
- Brainstorm ideas for conscious acts of kindness.
- Students record their acts of kindness in a journal or in an online group journal:
  - How did I make someone's day and what "that's not my job" job did I do?
  - How did I feel when doing these acts?
  - How did the person respond?
  - Any thoughts or "light bulb/aha" moments?

Name Speed

Intention: Build a culture of community.

- Students stand in a circle.
- One at a time, each student will say their name as fast as they can while the facilitator times them. Note that students cannot say their name until the person next to them is finished saying their own name.
- After students complete the first round, give students 30 seconds to come up with a strategy to do it faster. Repeat activity.

Three Things That Make You Human

Intention: Practice connecting with others.

- Students share three things that make them human.
- Many answers are not tangible (e.g., the fact that I make mistakes, I have the capacity to think, and I have the ability to love).
- Discuss how many of these answers are not tangible. Also, many answers will relate to connection.

Two Truths and a Lie

Intention: Practice connecting with others.

- Students are in groups of two.
- Student A tells Student B two truths and one lie about themselves.
- Student B guesses which is the lie.
- Switch roles.

Group Share/Fish Bowl

Intention: Practice receiving, reflection, and communication.

- Students share ideas with class (the ideas might be regarding an upcoming assignment or project).

One Word/Six Words

Intention: Practice reflection and communication.

- Each student says one word that summarizes the day, illustrating how they are feeling or what they are thinking.

Pair Share

Intention: Practice reflection and communication.

- Students share ideas with a partner.

Ultimately, we should see ourselves as a whole being because seeing ourselves as fragmented parts ignores the connection between the physical, emotional, social, mental, and spiritual components of our lives. We cannot ignore the idea that our health includes our mental states and social environment, seeing beyond our physical wellness and acknowledging the connection of our mind, body, spirit, and environments. Remember the last time you had a very good day of pampering yourself or doing something special for yourself. Maybe you had your hair styled, a massage, a manicure and/or a pedicure; took some quiet time where you could reflect or engage in devotion and affirmation; read a good book, watched an engaging movie, ate a tasty meal, and/or engaged in great conversation; or finally purchased something you had wanted for a while. What is it about those moments that makes you think fondly of them? Would you say that these moments contributed to your wellness and well-being? Finding joy in our present moment and finding our center contribute to our well-being, which is our balance and subjective perceptions on a variety of positive and/or negative states (e.g., happiness, life satisfaction, functioning, and vitality) in our lives (Baumeister et al., 2013; Huta & Ryan, 2010), which can lead us to a state of release, relaxation, and focus.

Helping a student understand how the domains of their lives are connected and impact them as well as how to cope during stressful or uncertain times, such as through the use of mindful activities, are integral for their success. With increased self-awareness and the use of mindfulness skills, students can discover how to meet life's challenges in a way that works best for them. Higher education professionals can teach mindfulness strategies to or use mindfulness strategies with college students to support them through difficult moments and spaces.

REFERENCES

American College Health Association (2018, Spring). *American College Health Association—National College Health Assessment II: Reference Group Executive Summary Spring 2018*. Silver Spring, MD: Author. Retrieved August 11, 2019, from https://www.acha.org/documents/ncha/NCHA-II_Spring_2018_Reference_Group_Executive_Summary.pdf

Arnett, J. J. (2004). *Emerging Adulthood: The Winding Road from the Late Teens through the Twenties*. Oxford University Press.

Balaswamy, S., & Richardson, V. E. (2001). The cumulative effects of life event, personal and social resources on subjective well-being of elderly widowers. *International Journal of Aging and Human Development, 53*, 311–327. https://doi.org/10.2190/6TY3-FX64-K8P4-KBPQ

Baumeister, R. F., & Leary, M. R. (1995). The need to belong: Desire for interpersonal attachments as a fundamental human motivation. *Psychological Bulletin, 117*(3), 497–529. https://doi.org/10.1037/0033-2909.117.3.497

Baumeister, R. F., Vohs, K. D., Aaker, J. L., & Garbinsky, E. N. (2013). Some key differences between a happy life and a meaningful life. *The Journal of Positive Psychology, 8*, 505–516. https://doi.org/10.1080/17439760.2013.830764

Bedrosian, T. A., & Nelson, R. J. (2017). Timing of light exposure affects mood and brain circuits. *Translational Psychiatry, 7*(1), e1017, 1–9. https://doi.org/10.1038/tp.2016.262

Berson, D. M., Dunn, F. A., & Takao, M. (2002). Phototransduction by retinal ganglion cells that set the circadian clock. *Science, 295*(5557), 1070–1073. https://doi.org/10.1126/science.1067262

Boals, A., & Banks, J. B. (2020, May 28). Stress and cognitive functioning during a pandemic: Thoughts from stress researchers. *Psychological Trauma: Theory, Research, Practice, and Policy, 12*(S1), S255–S257. http://dx.doi.org/10.1037/tra0000716

Brandy, J. M., Penckofer, S., Solari-Twadell, P. A., & Velsor-Friedrich, B. (2015). Factors predictive of depression in first-year college students. *Journal of Psychosocial Nursing and Mental Health Services, 53*(2), 38–44. https://doi.org/10.3928/02793695-20150126-03

Brown, I. W., & Ryan, R. M. (2003). The benefits of being present: Mindfulness and its role in psychological well-being. *Journal of Personality and Social Psychology, 84*(4), 822–848. https://doi.org/10.1037/0022-3514.84.4.822

Burke, M. G., Laves, K., Sauerheber, J. D., & Hughey, A. W. (2020). *Helping College Students in Distress: A Faculty Guide.* Routledge. https://doi.org/10.4324/9780367815738

Burke, M. G., Sauerheber, J. D., Hughey, A. W., & Laves, K. (2017). *Helping Skills for Working with College Students: Applying Counseling Theory to Student Affairs Practice.* Routledge. https://doi.org/10.4324/9781315650531

Cashwell, C. S., Bentley, D. P., & Bigbee, A. (2007). Spirituality and counselor wellness. *Journal of Humanistic Counseling, Education and Development, 46*(1), 66–81.

Chiu, L., Emblen, J. D., Hofwegen, L. V., Sawatzky, R., & Meyerhoff, H. (2004). An integrative review of the concept of spirituality in the health sciences. *Western Journal of Nursing Research, 26*(4), 405–428. https://doi.org/10.1177/0193945904263411

Christakis, N. A., & Fowler, J. H. (2009). *Connected: The Surprising Power of Our Social Networks and How They Shape Our Lives.* Little, Brown and Company.

Cress, V. C., & Lampman, C. (2007). Hardiness, stress, and health-promoting behaviors among college students. *Psi Chi Journal of Undergraduate Research, 12*(1), 18–23. https://doi.org/10.24839/1089-4136.JN12.1.18

Cristina, E. D. (2004). Understanding true aromatherapy: Understanding essential oils. *Home Health Care Management & Practice, 16*(6), 474–479. https://doi.org/10.1177/1084822304265851

Currie, C. L., Wild, T. C., Schopflocher, D. P., Laing, L., & Veugelers, P. (2012). Racial discrimination experienced by Aboriginal university students in Canada. *Canadian Journal of Psychiatry, 57*(10), 617–625. https://doi.org/10.1177/070674371205701006

Dispenza, J. (2007). *Evolve Your Brain: The Science of Changing Your Mind*. Health Communications, Inc.

Dyer, W. W. (2004). *The Power of Intention*. Hay House, Inc.

Elliot, A. J., & Maier, M. A. (2007). Color and psychological functioning. *Current Directions in Psychological Science, 16*(5), 250–254. https://doi.org/10.1111/j .1467-8721.2007.00514.x

Fernandez, D. C., Fogerson, P. M., Ospri, L. L., Zhao, H., Berson, D. M., & Hattar, S. (2018). Light affects mood and learning through distinct retina–brain pathways, *Cell, 175*(1), 71–84. https://doi.org/10.1016/j.cell.2018.08.004

Freeman, L. (2009). *Mosby's Complementary & Alternative Medicine: A Research-Based Approach* (3rd edition). Elsevier.

Galderisi, S., Heinz, A., Kastrup, M., Beezhold, J., & Sartorius, N. (2015). Toward a new definition of mental health. *World Psychiatry: Official Journal of the World Psychiatric Association (WPA), 14*(2), 231–233. https://doi.org/10.1002/wps.20231

Glasser, W. (2000). *Counseling with Choice Theory*. HarperCollins.

Hattar, S., Liao, H. W., Takao, M., Berson, D. M., & Yau, K. W. (2002). Melanopsin-containing retinal ganglion cells: Architecture, projections, and intrinsic photo-sensitivity. *Science, 295*(5557), 1065–1070. https://doi.org/10.1097/00007611 -198606000-00022

Hettler, W. (1984). Wellness: Encouraging a lifetime pursuit of excellence. *Health Values, 8*(4), 13–17.

Hiatt, J. (1986). Spirituality, medicine, and healing. *Southern Medical Journal, 79*(6), 736–743. https://doi.org/10.1097/00007611-198606000-00022

Hidayetoglu, M. L., Yildirim, K., & Akalin, A. (2012). The effects of color and light on indoor wayfinding and the evaluation of the perceived environment. *Journal of Environmental Psychology, 32*(2012), 50–58. https://doi.org/10.1016/j.jenvp.20 11.09.001

Holt-Lunstad, J., Smith, T. B., Baker, M., Harris, T., & Stephenson, D. (2015). Loneliness and social isolation as risk factors for mortality: A meta-analytic review. *Perspectives on Psychological Science, 10*(2), 227–237. https://doi.org/10 .1177/1745691614568352

Huta, V., & Ryan, R. M. (2010). Pursuing pleasure or virtue: The differential and over-lapping well-being benefits of hedonic and eudaimonic motives. *Journal of Happiness Studies, 11*, 735–762. https://doi.org/10.1007/s10902-009-9171-4

Kabat-Zinn, J. (1991). *Full Catastrophe Living: Using the Wisdom of Your Body and Mind to Face Stress, Pain, and Illness*. Dell Publishing.

Kabat-Zinn, J. (2003). Mindfulness-based interventions in context: Past, present, and future. *Clinical Psychology: Science and Practice, 10*(2), 144–156. https://doi.org /10.1093/clipsy.bpg016

Kingston, K. (2016). *Clear Your Clutter with Feng Shui: Free Yourself from Physical, Mental, Emotional, and Spiritual Clutter Forever* (revised and updated). Harmony Books.

Klinger, E. (1977). *Meaning and Void: Inner Experience and the Incentives in People's Lives.* University of Minnesota Press.

Klinger, E. (1998). The search for meaning in evolutionary perspective and its clinical implications. In P. Wong & P. Fry (Eds.), *The Human Quest for Meaning: A Handbook of Psychological Research and Clinical Applications* (pp. 27–50). Lawrence Erlbaum.

Kitzrow, M. A. (2003). The mental health needs of today's college students: Challenges and recommendations, *NASPA Journal, 41*(1), 167–181. https://doi.org/10.2202/0027-6014.1310

Knez, I., & Kers, C. (2000). Effects of indoor lighting, gender, and age on mood and cognitive performance. *Environment and Behavior, 32*(6), 817–831. https://doi.org/10.1177/0013916500326005

Koenig, H. G., McCullough, M., & Larson, D. B. (2000). *Handbook of Religion and Health.* Oxford University Press. https://doi.org/10.1093/acprof:oso/9780195118667.001.0001

Lambert, N. M., Stillman, T. F., Hicks, J. A., Kamble, S., Baumeister, R. F., & Fincham, F. D. (2013). To belong is to matter: Sense of belonging enhances meaning in life. *Personality and Social Psychology Bulletin, 39*(11), 1418–1427. https://doi.org/10.1177/0146167213499186

Lee, M. S., Lee, J., Park, B. J., & Miyazaki, Y. (2015). Interaction with indoor plants may reduce psychological and physiological stress by suppressing autonomic nervous system activity in young adults: A randomized crossover study. *Journal of Physiological Anthropology, 34*(1), 21. https://doi.org/10.1186/s40101-015-0060-8

LeViness, P., Bershad, C., & Gorman, K. (2017). *The Association for University and College Counseling Center Directors Annual Survey.* Retrieved August 1, 2019, from https://taucccd.memberclicks.net/assets/documents/Governance/2017%20aucccd%20survey-public-apr26.pdf

Maslow, A. H. (1943). Theory of human motivation. *Psychological Review, 50*, 370–396. https://doi.org/10.1037/h0054346

McKay, M., Wood, J. C., & Brantley, J. (2007). *The Dialectical Behavior Therapy Skills Workbook.* New Harbinger.

Mehranfar, M., Younesi, J., & Banihashem, A. (2012). Effectiveness of mindfulness-based cognitive therapy on reduction of depression and anxiety symptoms in mothers of children with cancer. *Iranian Journal of Cancer Prevention, 5*(1), 1–9.

Menninghaus, W., Wagner, V., Wassiliwizky, E., Schindler, I., Hanich, J., Jacobsen, T., & Koelsch, S. (2019). What are aesthetic emotions? *Psychological Review, 126*(2), 171–195. https://doi.org/10.1037/rev0000135

Molasso, W. R. (2006). Measuring a student's sense of purpose in life. *Michigan Journal of College Student Development, 12*, 15–24.

NASA (n.d.). Plants clean air and water for indoor environments. *NASA Spinoff*. Retrieved July 29, 2020, from https://spinoff.nasa.gov/Spinoff2007/ps_3.html

Ostrove, J. M., & Long, S. M. (2007). Social class and belonging: Implications for college adjustment. *Review of Higher Education*, *30*(4), 363–389. https://doi.org/10.1353/rhe.2007.0028

Pert, C. (1997). *Molecules of Emotion*. Scribner.

Sansone, R. A., & Sansone, L. A. (2013). Sunshine, serotonin, and skin: A partial explanation for seasonal patterns in psychopathology? *Innovations in Clinical Neuroscience*, *10*(7–8), 20–24.

Siegel, D. (2020). *The Developing Mind: How Relationships and the Brain Interact to Shape Who We Are*. The Guilford Press.

Siegel, D. J. (2012). *Pocket Guide to Interpersonal Neurobiology: An Integrative Handbook of the Mind*. W.W. Norton & Co.

Smith, W. A. (2009). Campus wide climate: Implications for African American students. In L. Tillman (Ed.), *A Handbook of African American Education* (pp. 297–309). Sage. https://doi.org/10.4135/9781412982788.n18

Solloway, S. (2000). Contemplative practitioners, presence or the project of thinking gaze differently. *Encounter, Education for Meaning and Social Justice*, *13*(3), 30–36.

Stephens, T., Dulberg, C., & Joubert, N. (1999). Mental health of the Canadian population: A comprehensive analysis. *Chronic Diseases in Canada*, *20*(3), 118–126.

Steger, M. F. (2012). Experiencing meaning in life: Optimal functioning at the nexus of well-being, psychopathology, and spirituality. In P. T. P. Wong & P. S. Fry (Eds.), *Handbook of Personal Meaning: Theory, Research, and Application* (2nd ed., pp. 165–184). Lawrence Earlbaum. https://doi.org/10.1080/17439760802303127

Steger, M. F., Oishi, S., & Kashdan, T. B. (2009). Meaning in life across the life span: Levels and correlates of meaning in life from emerging adulthood to older adulthood. *Journal of Positive Psychology*, *4*, 43–52. https://doi.org/10.1111/0022-4537.00149

Stone, N. J. (2003). Environmental view and color for a simulated telemarketing task. *Journal of Environmental Psychology*, *23*, 63–78. https://doi.org/10.1016/S0272-4944(02)00107-X

Stone, N. J., & English, A. J. (1998). Task type, posters, and workspace color on mood, satisfaction and performance. *Journal of Environmental Psychology*, *18*, 175–185. https://doi.org/10.1006/jevp.1998.0084

Strayhorn, T. (2012). *College Students' Sense of Belonging: A Key to Educational Success for All Students*. Routledge. https://doi.org/10.4324/9780203118924

Thoits, P. A. (2011). Mechanisms linking social ties and support to physical and mental health. *Journal of Health and Social Behavior*, *52*, 145–161. https://doi.org/10.1177/0022146510395592

Varney, E., & Buckle, J. (2013). Effect of inhaled essential oils on mental exhaustion and moderate burnout: A small pilot study. *The Journal of Alternative and Complementary Medicine*, *19*(1), 69–71. https://doi.org/10.1089/acm.2012.0089

Witmer, J. M., & Sweeney, T. J. (1992). A holistic model for wellness and prevention over the life span. *Journal of Counseling & Development*, *71*(2), 140–148. https://doi.org/10.1002/j.1556-6676.1992.tb02189.x

World Health Organization. (2018, March 30). *Mental Health: Strengthening Our Response.* Retrieved February 20, 2019, from https://www.who.int/news-room/fact-sheets/detail/mental-health-strengthening-our-response.

Young, C., & Koopsen, C. (2005). *Spirituality, Health and Healing.* Slack Incorporated.

Chapter 2

Brain Basics

At the start of each semester, I (Dr Dye) ask students about their comfort, confidence, and knowledge in their relationships with their brains. Most, if not all, respond that they know little about their brains and how they work—although throughout their entire pre-K–12 academic life, they were often told to "think" and "use your brains" but never taught about the brain or "how" to use it. The image below depicts what I perceive as students describe their educational experiences—little support for a student's social/emotional and physical growth with more emphasis on the student's cognitive growth without allowing them to learn about the brain and how it works.

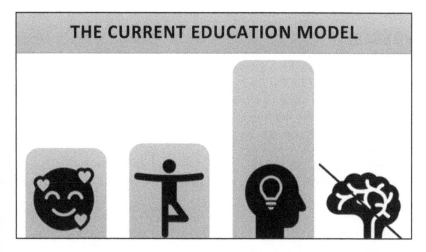

THE CURRENT EDUCATION MODEL

Teaching students at all educational levels about how the brain operates and how it can be used to control their cognitive and emotional health as well as their learning is empowerment. Accordingly, higher education professionals should begin to have conversations about how teaching students about how the brain functions could help them improve their process for organizing projects, studying, handling stress, and performing tasks. To begin the discussion about moving students toward strategies to help them with daily functioning and getting through stressful moments, an understanding about the basics of the brain must occur.

A FACULTY'S VOICE

I think that learning brain basics and how these concepts relate to stress are tremendous tenets for incoming students as many have not attained the ability to study and learn at the collegiate level or recognize how these concepts relate to their course scheduling and daily functioning. Sharing such information would be ideal in a course that serves an introductory purpose for first-time, first-year incoming students. There is also an opportunity for faculty to participate in Orientation and Career Development activities by sponsoring a workshop that shares information about the connection of brain basics, stress, and self-regulation.

—An associate professor at a university

THE BRAIN

The brain is an amazing organ generated by interactions in the world, and even more wonderful is the fact that each of our brains is generated in its own special way. It is brilliant how quadrillion moments of change occur within each person's life that account for the miraculous person that we each become. Every skill learned, every piece of you, and every action is a product of this change. This is neuroplasticity in action.

Neuroplasticity, also known as brain plasticity, is the bi-directional (incline or decline) as well as structural and functional ability of the brain to change throughout a person's life. It encompasses

a. Structural neuroplasticity, which is the brain's ability to change its physical structure as a result of learning;

b. Functional neuroplasticity, which is the brain's ability to move functions from a damaged area of the brain to an undamaged area.

Broadly defined, neuroplasticity includes our nervous system's ability to respond to intrinsic and extrinsic stimuli by reorganizing its structure, function and connections at many levels, from molecular to cellular to systems to behavior (Cramer et al., 2011). The complex nature of our brain and its networks gives rise to our uniqueness.

Several variables and characteristics play a role in this phenomenon of plasticity. One variable is that our brain reacts with every positive or negative thought, emotional stimulus, or physical action. For example, our personal experiences, especially interpersonal relationships during infancy and childhood, powerfully differentiate our neurology. One size does not fit all, since your brain is the result of the negative and positive experiences of your own life. What we think and how we think about things are a part of altering the structure and function of the brain regions (Perry, 2013; Siegel, 2020). Such core knowledge about our brain's ability and power can help higher education professionals understand the underlying basis for supporting college students with learning, coping, connection, and transition.

Each student who walks onto a university campus comes with a unique, tailored brain that will impact their college experience and learning. Can we imagine how empowering and liberating the learning experience could be for a student if they were able to identify and own a practical understanding of the varied parts of the brain and its function in their life of learning?

Let's explore some basic facts about the structure and function of the brain.

Our physical brain, with the consistency of jello or a soft-boiled egg, is housed in a protective skull that weighs only about 2–3 pounds and contains over 100 billion neurons. Structurally, our brain—often called the *triune* brain —consists of three main integral systems—the reptilian brain (instinctual), the mammalian or limbic brain (emotional), the monkey brain, and the human brain or neocortex (rational) (Davidson & Begley, 2013). However, more recent neuroscience brain function discourse has encouraged a "quadrune mind model" (Gibson, 2018; Shadid, 2020) and/or the "embodied brain model" (Siegel, 2020). Both the "quadrune mind model" and the "embodied brain model" build from the triune brain and appeal to more distinct aspects of the functionality, development, and bodily interconnection of the brain. For the sake of simplicity in introducing the brain, we will describe the triune model. This model is a good-to-know guide relevant to a college student's brain.

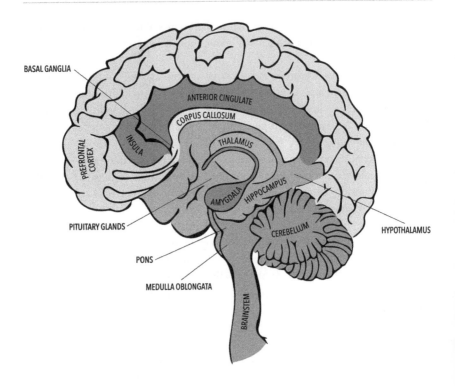

STRUCTURE AND FUNCTION OF THE BRAIN

The following discussion will start at the bottom and move up, emphasizing the structure and functions that are most important when working with students. Also, this flow is consistent with the order of the ancient evolution of the brain.

Reptilian Brain/Institutional (Lizard Brain)/ Cerebellum and Brain Stem

The brain stem, the oldest part of the head-brain, is the mass of tissue and nerves that sit at the bottom of the brain, connecting to the spinal cord. It plugs the brain (central nervous system) into the rest of the body through the spinal cord (peripheral nervous system). It is a major relay station for information coming back and forth between body and brain. The brain stem and lower structure functions are fundamental as they control all instinctual actions like breathing, heart rate, feeding/digestion, reproduction reflexive behaviors, and muscle control.

This area of the brain is also key to survival as it is responsible for the fight-flight-freeze-faint response, which is simply the body's automatic reaction to threat or stress. It helps us fight danger, flee from it, freeze when faced with it, or faint from it. More details of the fight-flight- freeze-faint response will be discussed in Chapter 4. This part of the brain contributes in an important way to the functioning of college students. Below is a list of parts of the brain with details related to their contribution to our state of being and thus to students' well-being.

The Cerebellum

A major structure of the hindbrain near the brainstem that regulates movement and voluntary motor skills such as physical balance, coordination, posture, and speech.

> **Plain and Simple:** Because of the cerebellum, students can stand upright and move their muscles while keeping balance during activities and events. The student riding a skateboard through campus in a smooth manner, where it appears that they are almost floating on water, is utilizing their cerebellum powers. Such actions are helpful for students to engage in physical activity that assists in maintaining their physical health and well-being.

The Medulla Oblongata

The medulla oblongata is located at the point where the brainstem connects to the spinal cord. It ensures vital involuntary functions such as the cardiovascular and respiratory systems and is responsible for reflexive actions such as vomiting, swallowing, coughing, and sneezing.

> **Plain and Simple:** As a student's brain can be so busy or easily distracted, if breathing were a voluntary act, they would probably forget to do it. It is a gift that there is a natural regulation (rate, rhythm, and tone) of breath as a function of the medulla oblongata. If a student is experiencing a high level of stress or panic and begins to breathe fast and excessively, the medulla oblongata is helpful as it notices the change in breathing and body's need for regulated breathing and then sends signals to the respiratory muscles involved in breathing to decrease the ventilation rate so carbon dioxide levels and pH can return to normal levels, as can the pons, which controls the rate of breathing. When a student becomes stressed or anxious and short of breath due to fast breathing, a breathing exercise can ease their symptoms, and doing the exercise daily can assist in preventing this physical reaction.

Pons

A large rounded bulgy structure that connects the medulla and the midbrain, the pons is home to cranial nerves that carry information about sensations such as touch, pain,

33

and temperature; motor commands dealing with eye movement; and chewing and facial expressions.

Plain and Simple: Students are able to enjoy the nourishments of the campus cafeteria and make the corresponding facial expression (facial nerve) because of the nerves that originate in the pons. They are also able to enjoy a sweet kiss to the cheek (trigeminal nerve), a whisper in the ear (vestibulocochlear nerve), and then look side to side (abducens nerve) while blushing because of nerves that originate in the pons.

Hypothalamus

This pearl-sized control center keeps one in a healthful, balanced bodily state (homeostasis). It regulates hunger, thirst, sleep, and sexual response and plays a role in controlling blood pressure, emotions, and secretion of hormones.

Plain and Simple: Although small in size, the hypothalamus is a big deal. It is literally the body's thermostat. When the body is too hot, it tells the body to sweat, and if too cold, it tells the body to shiver. The hypothalamus also signals the body to eat, drink, and sleep. The hypothalamus, which senses a change in our body, helps students realize when they have eaten enough, need to drink water, and need to get some rest. Therefore, when we tell students to "listen to your body," understanding how the hypothalamus works provides a framework for understanding this adage. Promoting students' awareness of their body and understanding of hunger cues, how their emotions influence eating decisions, and how stress manifests in their body can be beneficial.

The circadian rhythm, which is governed by a group of neurons called the suprachiasmatic nucleus located in the hypothalamus and is referred to as our master clock, translates cues from our environment into instructions for the body. The associated processes vacillate in predictable patterns each 24-hour day. As such, the circadian rhythm helps determine when we feel energized or exhausted at different times of the day. For college students, syncing class times to circadian rhythms can be beneficial. For example, a misalignment between a student's circadian rhythm and the student's environment can result in learning and attention deficits (Smarr & Schirmer, 2018). It is best that a student's time of peak alertness is not at odds with work, school, or other demands. Our brains, thanks to our inner clock, work at an optimum level at some point during the day depending on when we feel most energized to work and accordingly, we can be categorized in one of three chronotypes—a lark, hummingbird, or owl (Medina, 2014). Larks, also called early chronotypes, make up about one in ten students.

On the other end of the sleep spectrum, which also includes about one in ten students, is the late chronotype also known as owls (Medina, 2014). The rest of the student population is called hummingbirds, and true to the idea of a continuum, a hummingbird can be somewhere between the lark and owl. To maximize your productivity, try to set your schedule to match your chronotype. When advising students, it could be advantageous to take into account, if possible, what time of day that particular student will be most capable of learning and most alert.

CHRONOTYPES

(Medina, 2014)

Most productive a few hours before lunch
Most alert around noon
Do not need alarm clock
Often wake before 6:00 a.m.
Favorite mealtime is breakfast
Generally, consumes less coffee than non-larks
Most larks go to bed (or want to go to bed) by 9pm

LARK

Sleep patterns can "hover" across the continuum
Some are more owlish, some are more larkish and some are in between
Switches schedules regularly and may not feel any negative side effects

HUMMINGBIRD

Most alert around 6pm
Most productive in late evening
Rarely want to go to bed before 3:00 a.m.
Need an alarm clock
Extreme owls need multiple alarms to ensure arousal
If had their way, most owls would not wake before 10:00 a.m.
Favorite mealtime is dinner
If given opportunity, an owl would probably drink a lot of coffee daily to prop themselves up
Usually accumulate massive "sleep debt" as they go through life

OWL

Thalamus

The thalamus is the relay station/gateway for incoming sensory information from the spinal cord and brainstem. The sensation is then passed on to the cerebral cortex to determine location, type, and duration (i.e., touch, pain, or temperature).

Plain and Simple: In the early days of telephone operations, a switchboard operator answered incoming calls, received the information from the caller, and connected them to the correct extension using a switchboard. The thalamus is the body's switchboard operator. It is responsible for receiving sensory (i.e., touch, pain, or temperature) information, interpreting the information, and making the proper connections. Ninety-eight percent of all sensory input is relayed by the thalamus. The hypothalamus helps us find a comfortable, ideal temperature in a space, one that is not too hot and not too cold, but just right. For college students, these connections can help them find a suitable place to study or engage in a study group.

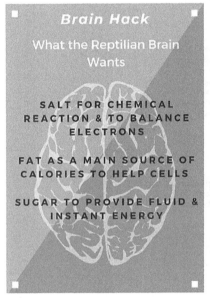

Brain Hack

What the Reptilian Brain Wants

SALT FOR CHEMICAL REACTION & TO BALANCE ELECTRONS

FAT AS A MAIN SOURCE OF CALORIES TO HELP CELLS

SUGAR TO PROVIDE FLUID & INSTANT ENERGY

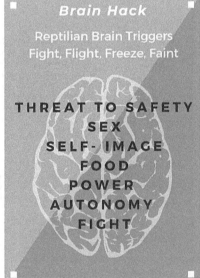

Brain Hack

Reptilian Brain Triggers Fight, Flight, Freeze, Faint

THREAT TO SAFETY
SEX
SELF-IMAGE
FOOD
POWER
AUTONOMY
FIGHT

MIDDLE BRAIN/EMOTIONAL (MAMMALIAN BRAIN)

Due to its development during the early evolution of man, the middle brain is often referred to as the paleomammalian brain or mammalian brain. This region of the brain is composed of structures that are central to a student's motivation, memories, emotions (attachments), and goal-directed behavior and arousal.

Basal Ganglia

The basal ganglia include masses of tissue/group of structures found deep in the cerebral hemisphere involved with rewards, stimulation seeking, and movement.

Plain and Simple: The basal ganglia are hypothesized to inhibit unwanted jerky movements. When a student reaches for a pencil, it is because of the basal ganglia that the movement is smooth and fluid and not jerky. The basal ganglia call all of the shots when you are outstretching your arm to reach for something or using your legs to take a flight of stairs. In addition, when a student deems that they are either rewarded or punished for a given behavior, the basal ganglia keep a record of this perception, and the student will automatically stop or be motivated to continue engaging in certain actions.

Hippocampus

This is a cluster of neurons shaped like a horseshoe that forms new memories and detects threats. The hippocampus is known for its role in forming, organizing, and processing memories, which includes all past knowledge and experiences.

Plain and Simple: Memories processed by the hippocampus keep us alive. Memory has provided students with information on where to find the food (food court), where to find shelter (their room in their residence hall), and where threats or challenges (classroom) may exist. It connects the smell of grandma's pie to a memory of a good time or the sound of opening the front door to a visit of a good friend. Most relevant to working with college students is the hippocampus' declarative memory. Declarative memory involves something you can declare, intentional recollection of facts and events, conscious recall. This ability involves four steps: encoding, storing, retrieving, and forgetting. Being able to form new memories about facts or events is a necessity and benefit for college students.

College students look to crack the code of storing and retrieving facts and information. Higher education professionals can help college students better encode, store, and retrieve information. Two suggestions to accomplish this task are presented here.

1. To form a robust memory, offer multifaceted information, imbued with emotion and the opportunity for students to experience their own

meaning-making about the topic. For example, you can ask a student to define a word and to include a personal experience, image, or song relevant to the word.

2. Offer students the same environmental conditions at retrieval of information as they were with initial learning. For example, if a lesson is taught and the learner is in a particular mood with the sun shining and gentle music playing softly, they will recall it better if, at retrieval, the same context exists.

Amygdala

An almond-shaped structure that regulates primal drives such as fear, pleasure, and hunger and how to respond to threatening events in the environment. It makes oxytocin and activates the pineal gland, which monitors hormones and releases endorphins (e.g., painkillers and anti-depressants). The amygdala also determines which memories are stored and where the memories are stored in the brain.

Plain and Simple: As the amygdala is a major hub of emotional activity, it is key to how students process strong emotions like fear and pleasure. Heightened activation in the amygdala reflects an important characteristic of behaviorally inhibited students—they usually show up to class hypervigilant and are constantly on the lookout for potential threats and perceived sources of danger. Often referred to as an amygdala hijack, if emotions are too aroused, the person loses control of their behaviors.

GOOD HORMONE (CHEMICAL MESSENGERS) HACK

ENDORPHIN
THE PAIN KILLER

- Laughter
- Essential Oil
- Dark Chocolate
- Exercise / Dance
- Mind/ Body Movement - Yoga
- Conversation with a good friend

OXYTOCIN
THE LOVE HORMONE

- Listen to music
- Play with a baby
- Hold hands with someone
- Hug someone
- Give a compliment
- Play with a pet

SEROTONIN
THE MOOD STABILIZER

- Meditate
- Sunshine
- Walk/ sit in nature
- Eat less processed sugar
- Practice gratitude
- Swim
- Cycle

DOPAMINE
THE REWARD CHEMICAL

- Get some rest
- Take a cold shower
- Visit a new place
- Make your bed
- Celebrate small wins

Pituitary Gland

Despite its small size, the pituitary gland influences nearly every part of a student's body. It receives signals from the hypothalamus in the form of hormones (our body's chemical messengers) which in turn control the production and release of further hormones in hormone-secreting glands and organs in the body. See the "Good Hormone Hack" box that follows.

Plain and Simple: There are some good hormones (chemical messengers) that come through the pituitary gland by way of the hypothalamus. Students can learn to hack these hormones for all the good feelings they need. The four most common are oxytocin, dopamine, serotonin, and endorphins.

Oxytocin, often called the hug or love hormone, is released during childbirth to promote mommy-and-baby attachment. It is released from the pituitary gland during social interactions such as hugs, good conversations, and laughter. When hugging or cuddling, there is a stimulation of pressure receptors under the skin that can activate the release of good hormones and, in turn, bring students to a more relaxed state. Research has shown that oxytocin can diminish inflammation in the body, lower blood pressure, and decrease heart rate and cortisol levels.

Dopamine and serotonin, the "happy hormones," both contribute to the regulation of a student's mood and emotion. Dopamine, specifically, plays a role in a student's perception of motivation and reward. Dopamine is released into a student's system when the brain detects an emotionally charged event and then it aids in the brain in storing the memory for future reference. While serotonin, like dopamine, helps to regulate mood, it also helps regulate temperature and appetite. However, too much or too little of either of these can cause physical and psychological symptoms.

Endorphins are in our body's natural pain relievers and pleasure boosters. They are released during activities like exercise, eating, and sex, but also in response to pain or stress.

NEW BRAIN/RATIONAL—PREFRONTAL CORTEX

The prefrontal cortex, located at the very front of the physical brain, was the last brain structure to develop in the course of evolution. Although it is not fully developed until the age of 25, it was and is known to be the site of highest or higher-order cognitive activity (Davidson & Begley, 2013). This region of the brain controls many of our behaviors that separate us from other animals (Medina, 2014). It is involved in the higher-order regulation of behavior and attention as we filter and suppress irrelevant information.

This portion of the brain is housed within the neo-cortex, the outer region of the brain within the cerebral cortex. This portion of the brain is also divided into two hemispheres. The left side of the brain is the language center and involves logical, linear, computing, and conscious thought processes. The right side of the brain is the area of creativity, spatial, intuitive, abstract, and subconscious thought processes. As higher education professionals and educators, while we may have been socialized to see this area of the brain as most important in a student's learning, it is actually only at its best when the other parts of the brain have been satisfied and cared for.

Medial Prefrontal Cortex

This area of the prefrontal cortex is involved in attending to challenging cognitive tasks, conflict resolution, bimanual coordination (skills that use two hands to complete), the body's perception of pain and the emotional response behind it as well as motivation as it relates to rewards and goals (Siddiqui, et al, 2008).

Plain and Simple: The medial prefrontal cortex is the key region involved in understanding self and others. It guides decision making in young adults while learning and predicting the likely outcomes of one's actions. The medial prefrontal cortex comes in handy when a student needs to engage in self-reflection, evaluate a situation, and make a choice that is most beneficial to them at that time. College students often engage in decision making, such as selecting a major, engaging in conflict resolution and goal setting, and choosing studying over socializing with others. It is also important as students should evaluate their decisions and hopefully learn from them.

Orbital prefrontal cortex

This area helps students control impulses and ignore distractions. It also plays a role in reward anticipation, expectations, and processing of outcomes even when a reward is not produced. This region has also been shown to control social and emotional behavior in order to follow social rules.

Plain and Simple: A student's presence in college (or any long-term commitment) is an example of their orbital prefrontal cortex's ability to forego small immediate rewards for larger delayed rewards. If you have observed the social media Fruit Snack Challenge, which is similar to the "marshmallow experiment" conducted by Mischel and colleagues, you saw a parent put a tempting snack in front of their child and then tells them they can have some, but the child needs to wait until the parent returns to the room. Similarly, can a college student give up the temptation of text message notifications and social media feeds while studying for an exam on which they need to perform well? If a student has impatience, poor planning, and/or impulsive behavior, they are likely to not persist in college because their behavior and judgment would not be conducive to waiting for the reward of earning their degree. Self-control and decision making are essential components to meeting goals.

Lateral prefrontal cortex

The lateral prefrontal cortex is critically involved in selective attention and execution of action. It is also great at directing and predicting consequences of actions.

> **Plain and Simple:** A student's ability to anticipate events in the environment is because of the lateral prefrontal cortex. As a student walks into a party and takes notice of the atmosphere, mood, and behaviors of others, they are able to anticipate if there is a possibility of a calm evening or a turbulent evening. Based on their attention to and assessment of the environment, they can then think about the potential consequences and select an action that they believe is best for them at that time. As college students will face pitfalls and uncomfortable issues, being able to focus their attention, predict possible consequences, and execute an action that is beneficial to their well-being can be significant tasks.

TAKE A MOMENT

Take a brief moment and ask yourself or others the following questions.

- What are my thoughts on being able to use my brain to alter stress and deal with difficult moments and trauma?
- What are some activities that I can use to exercise the brain "muscle" to gain cognitive flexibility and self-regulate?
- Considering the brain basics, do I believe that my emotions affect my actions, or do my actions affect my emotions, and why?

SUPPORTING PRE-FRONTAL CORTEX DEVELOPMENT

Essentially as young and emerging adults, college students have the ability to change their brains and grow healthier brains, which can occur throughout their lifespan regardless of age (Badenoch, 2008). Higher education professionals can play a role in helping students grow their brains, not simply learning academic or subject content but achieving good brain growth beyond the explicit curriculum. Students can create a personalized brain health plan based on an objective evaluation of their strengths and, especially, their weaknesses. The "Brain Growth Cheat Sheet" below provides information about our brain and how we can enhance its growth.

BRAIN GROWTH CHEAT SHEET

- Our brain builds a new association with each feeling, thought, and action. Visiting a new place, being exposed to a new skill, or learning a new skill (even if it is a small one) can remodel the brain and grow new pathways in the brain.
- Every new skill/ability creates your brain in that area. For example, as you acquired your ability to read, you created your very own reading brain. You can develop your own listening brain, drawing brain, etc.
- Whatever fires together, wires together. Take time daily to see and do positive things. Humankind is busy driving their brain in the negative direction.
- Train the brain to keep track of something during adversity. When working with noise in the environment, you can strengthen the ability to hold information while distractions occur. Adversities can sharpen the brain if they are acknowledged as such.
- *Blastic* = growing the brain and *clastic* = degeneration of the brain. Our modern culture is killing our brain health (clastic) when we sit at our computers or look at screens all day.
- To control the positive use of the brain, use less technology and limit the use of TV, phone, and GPS. The student without the bells and whistles of a "technology brain" is in a more valuable situation because they are required to practice more thinking, problem solving, and critical analysis.
- Challenges stimulate brain growth. Students can practice healthy brain habits when they allow themselves to perceive an event as a challenge instead of a threat.

BRAIN BASICS ACTIVITIES: PRACTICE AND INTENTION

The brain is involved in everything we do and influences many facets of our lives. Like any other part of the body that we want to be healthy and develop, the brain too needs to be cared for and exercised. Exercising the brain, as an individual or a group, by incorporating a few simple brain exercises into our daily lives, such as the suggested activities that follow, can be beneficial for us in many ways.

A Walk to Nowhere

Intention: Bring the brain joy and help unfreeze stress response with rhythmic activities. The brain likes rhythmic sequences.

Facilitator Prep: You will need a small- or medium-size hand drum with mallet/beater. These can be ordered online or found in a local music store.

Facilitator says:

- "Together we will move in a circle. This activity is called a Walk to Nowhere."
- Ask participants to form a circle and turn bodies so their left shoulder is in the circle. With the beat of the drum, starting with the right foot, everyone will take four steps forward and then four steps back. Then repeat. As the Instructor, you can demonstrate walking forward and back to the beat of four counts. The instructor invites the group to practice. Drumming and counting 1, 2, 3, 4 with each step while walking forward and counting 1, 2, 3, 4 while walking backward—eventually the instructor can discontinue saying a number until there is no need to count out loud.
- If students get distracted or step out of line, encourage sending gratitude to self and start again.
- Students continue walking four steps forward and four steps back until the facilitator stops drumming (average time 2–4 minutes depending on age).

Brain, Beat, Breath (3Bs)

Intention: To learn how to have an awareness of the connection of breath, heartbeat, and thoughts in the brain.

- Share with students that there is a way to find out if they are getting upset, stressed, or feel hurried with the 3Bs.
  1. Breath check
     - Place one hand on belly, one on chest, and close your eyes.
     - Ask yourself: Is my breath short and high in my chest or am I taking a full, long and deep breath in (inhalation) and deep breath out (exhalation) with a slight pause in between each?
  2. Beat check
     - With the pointer finger and the middle finger, locate pulse on the side of your neck.
     - Ask yourself: What is the strength and rhythm of my pulse? Is it fast and jumpy or slow and steady? By doing this regularly, an individual

gets to know pulse. The pulse can tell you a lot about one's heart, mind, and body.

3. Brain check
   - Close eyes and place hands on lap.
   - Ask yourself: What's going on in my brain? What kind of thoughts do I have right now? Are my thoughts positive (energizing) or negative (defeated)? Are my thoughts affecting the cycle of my breath or my pulse?
   - With our thoughts, we can speed up our breath and pulse or we can think calm thoughts and slow them down. As soon as we think a thought, our body responds.

Chime

Intention: To learn a strategy that calms our brains when the amygdala is firing. Practice tuning in and becoming centered.

Facilitator Prep: You will need a small chime or singing bowl. These can be ordered online or found in a local music store.

- Invite students to close eyes or allow gaze to fall to their lap.
- Facilitator rings the chime.
- Students listen to the chime.
- Students give a thumbs up when they can no longer hear the chime.

Drum Walk

Intention: To bring the brain joy and help unfreeze stress response with rhythmic activities. The brain likes rhythmic sequences.

Facilitator Prep: You will need a small- or medium-size hand drum with mallet/beater. These can be ordered online or found in a local music store.

- Students stand.
- The leader first begins drumming slowly and then gently speeds up.
- Students move freely through the room to the beat of the drum.
- While drumming, have the students observe what their thoughts/feelings are as the drum goes slowly/softly/quickly/loudly.
- Pause the group and have students place their hands on their hearts or check their pulse rate.
- Follow the same drumming format again while students move freely through the room.
- While drumming, have students notice how their heartbeat or pulse rate shifts.

45

- Pause the group and have students close their eyes and notice their breath, and if the breath starts low in the belly or high in the chest.

Eagle Pose

Intention: Engage the cerebellum, which facilitates the brain's ability to find center and gravity.

- Students stand tall with feet hip-width apart and toes forward. Take arms wide and then wrap arms around self, like giving a self-hug, right arm on top.
- Students bend knees as if sitting in a chair.
- Students lift their left leg off the floor and cross the left knee over the right knee.
- Students wrap their left foot around the right ankle or rest left toes on the ground like a kickstand.
- Students take three deep breaths.
- Repeat the same steps listed above for the right leg.
- Now release your leg and bend your knees again as if sitting in a chair.

Gratitude Letter

Intention: Practice gratitude and release good chemical messengers.
   Facilitator Prep: Purchase a pack of postcards or write letters on a piece of paper.

- Have students practice an act of kindness by writing a gratitude postcard to someone at the institution. This note might be for a friend, professor, custodian, residential advisor, or anyone who they see regularly at the institution.
- Review the parts of an effective compliment (e.g., is it true, is it kind, does it offer a specific strength) and elaborate with example.

Happy, Human, Why

Intention: Practice introspection, connecting, and gratitude reflection to release good chemical messengers.

- Students are in groups of two (or larger).
- Student A tells Student B what makes them happy, what makes them human, and what is their "why." There are no incorrect responses; this is an opportunity to practice and share open introspection.
- Switch roles.

Instant Replay

Intention: Build hippocampus activity to strengthen short-term memory skills. Repeating allows the brain to remember.

- The facilitator can open up the activity by asking students about their favorite sports team and what they know about an "instant replay."
- Students stand in a circle.
- Each student will say their name and do a gesture at the same time (i.e., hop on one foot).
- When the student is finished, the entire group will do an instant replay of the gesture, while saying the student's name (i.e., hop on one foot).
- Repeat until each student has said their name with a gesture.

Memorize the Movement

Intention: Build hippocampus activity to strengthen short-term memory skills.

- Students get into groups of six and ten.
- Each student is going to perform a task (clap hands three times, snap two times, pat legs five times, etc.).
- The goal is to complete each task in order around the circle.
- The game starts with one person performing a small task for the group.
- The next person repeats the previous task and adds their own task after.
- The next person repeats the first person's task and second person's task and then shows the group their task.
- The play continues around the group with each person performing and adding a new task until they make it back to the first person who started the game.
- If someone does not complete the sequence correctly, the group must start over. However, the entire group cheers when someone messes up, rather than rolling eyes or becoming upset.
- Emphasize that this is only a game and the importance of supporting one another, even if they make a mistake.

Wow or Wonder

Intention: Practice reflection and recall and engage prefrontal cortex desire to "want to know."

- Students reflect about the class/session/week and share their "wow or wonder."
  - "wow": feeling, thought, or favorite activity

- "wonder": any comments/questions that they want to think or know more about.

The road to our personal growth can start with understanding how our brains work. Everything we are, everything we do, and everything we will be are rooted in the complexity of our brain. The regions of our brain play a significant role in managing and regulating our involuntary functions, sensory data and signal relay, body movement and balance, intellectual functions, sensory impulses, controls, emotions, and internal functions. What's more, our brain's plasticity allows it to adapt and change, which can be beneficial when we are stressed and anxious. How long, where, and what we give attention to in our life creates our repetitive patterns that then create connections in the brain, allowing our thoughts to serve as significant contributors to stress and anxiety. Comprehending brain basics can aid higher educational professionals in teaching students about stress and how the brain responds. When students understand brain wiring, how thoughts influence neuropathway connections, and the connection between mind and body, they can feel empowered to make healthy choices and better cope with life's demands. As students learn how to create and strengthen neural pathway networks, they can engage in activities to grow healthier brains, which can help make them more flexible and adaptable to change. Just like a physical workout can train your body, a workout of your brain with brain activities can train your brain, improving regions associated with learning, memory, regulating emotions, focus, and per-spective. Higher education professionals can share information about how the brain is wired and how brain activities can improve an individual's well-being while reducing the symptoms of stress and anxiety.

REFERENCES

Badenoch, B. (2008). *Being a Brain-Wise Therapist: A Practical Guide to Interpersonal Neurobiology (Norton Series on Interpersonal Neurobiology)*. WW Norton & Company.

Cramer, S. C., Sur, M., Dobkin, B. H., O'Brien, C., Sanger, T. D., Trojanowski, J. Q., Rumsey, J. M., Hicks, R., Cameron, J., Chen, D., Chen, W. G., Cohen, L. G., deCharms, C., Duffy, C. J., Eden, G. F., Fetz, E. E., Filart, R., Freund, M., Grant, S. J., Haber, S., ... Vinogradov, S. (2011). Harnessing neuroplasticity for clinical applications. *Brain: A Journal of Neurology, 134*(6), 1591–1609. https://doi.org/10.1093/brain/awr039

Davidson, R. J., & Begley, S. (2013). *The Emotional Life of Your Brain: How Its Unique Patterns Affect The Way You Think, Feel, and Live—And How You Can Change Them*. Penguin Group.

Gibson, R. (2018). *Combining Brainspotting with Somatic Archaeology for Transgenerational Reconciliation*. Howling at the Moon Productions.

Medina, J. (2014). *Brain Rules: 12 Principles for Surviving and Thriving At Work, Home, and School* (2nd edition). Pear Press.

Perry, B. D. (2013). *Brief: Reflections on Childhood, Trauma and Society.* The ChildTrauma Academy Press.

Shadid, T. (2020). *Quadrune Mind: Neurospirituality and the Four Minds of the Human Brain Study Guide.* Retrieved from https://quadrunemind.com/wp-content/uploads/2 020/06/Quadrune-Mind-Study-Guide-by-Tom-F.-Shadid-Ph.D.-3.pdf

Siddiqui, S. V., Chatterjee, U., Kumar, D., Siddiqui, A., & Goyal, N. (2008). Neuropsychology of prefrontal cortex. *Indian Journal of Psychiatry, 50*(3), 202–208. https://doi.org/10.4103/0019-5545.43634

Siegel, D. (2020). *The Developing Mind: How Relationships and the Brain Interact to Shape Who We Are* (3rd edition). Guilford Press.

Smarr, B. L., & Schirmer, A. E. (2018). 3.4 million real-world learning management system logins reveal the majority of students experience social jet lag correlated with decreased performance. *Scientific Reports, 8,* 4793. https://doi.org/10.1038 /s41598-018-23044-8

Chapter 3

Relax and Release

We are all very much a product of our cultural environment. This can be seen by simply observing the skills of children across the globe—we might observe a little boy bouncing a ball on his head in Argentina while a child in Cuba creates a baseball bat and ball with a stick and rock. We can even consider how with the shift from an agrarian society came the new demand for reading. In this shift, we have observed that literacy difficulties such as dyslexia became a new problem. Since we view the world through the lens of our experiences and beliefs, which other individuals and institutions influence, we become conditioned to behave and make choices accordingly. Therefore, we tend to adapt to what our cultural environment presents to us. Modern life appears to move quickly and requires a lot of multitasking; so, we move quickly and multitask.

Today, we live in an overscheduled, fast-paced, performance-based world, and now we see stress as a new problem. How we experience our abilities, skills, and mental wellness is very much a function of the expectations and demands of our societal culture. Stress occurs when environmental demands exceed an individual's perception of their ability to cope. As Fink (2016) noted, stress is "a highly personalized phenomenon that varies between people depending on individual vulnerability and resilience, and between different types of tasks" (p. 3). With so many occurrences and issues, personal or societal, that are present today—e.g., pandemic, healthcare costs, financial obligations, politics, race relations—and the many responsibilities most people face—e.g., work, family, education, debt, and wellness—there should be little surprise that stress seems to be prevalent in the United States. Let's consider the findings of the 12th annual Stress in America survey (2018) conducted by the American Psychological Association (APA):

- Nearly three-quarters of adults are suffering from moderate to high levels of stress and report experiencing at least one symptom of stress in the past month.

- Two-thirds of U.S. adults cited the cost of health insurance as a stressor.
- More than 6 in 10 Americans (62 percent) reported our current political climate as a stressor.
- Nearly, one-quarter (24 percent) of adults identified discrimination as a significant source of stress.
- Work, money, and the economy have consistently topped the list over the 12 years of the survey as a source of significant stress for two-thirds (64 percent) of U.S. Americans.

Reports of stress are even higher when we look specifically at college-age adults. More than 8 out of 10 (81 percent) adults between the ages of 18 and 21 reported money as the most significant stressor, with as many (77 percent) reporting the same about work. Almost a third of college-age individuals are stressed about basic elements and necessities of life such as money, debt, and housing stability.

Stress is a normal physical and psychological function; however, it too often interferes with our daily life functions. In college, stress creates inefficiency in a student's productivity in their daily tasks. Stress makes us repeat without purpose—for example, as students read the week's chapter reading for their English course—but when under stress, the brain is cycling with ten other things. Therefore, the student might possibly reread one page four or five times because they are not retaining any words and are simply scanning the page. Stress can make us feel out of sync or physically unwell,

A STUDENT'S VOICE

I find myself pausing to take calming and grounding breaths throughout my day to help me release stress, negativity and tension. Mindfulness has been extremely useful in my parenting practices as well.

—An undergraduate student

TYPES OF STRESS

All stress is not created equal. There are three different types of stress that we can define based on a) how it comes on; b) symptoms associated with it; and c) duration. The three types of stress are acute stress, chronic stress, and psychological stress.

Acute Stress

- Usually brief
- Can show up in anyone's life
- Is the most common and frequent stress presentation

We are humans that solve problems for our survival; our human stress response is built for some stress. However, we are built for stress that only last seconds, not months or years. Therefore, stress that is acute can sometimes be good for students. It keeps us motivated and on our toes. This good stress is also called *eustress*. It brings a healthy level of pressure, motivation, focus, energy, and performance that stretches a student in a new way. For most students, if the stress is not too severe, the brain actually performs better under this type of pressure. Students need to uncouple the idea of having a lot to do and being extremely stressed out about it. They are actually two separate things, but we often combine them and confuse them.

Healthy Acute Stress:
A student being invited to the front of the class by a professor for a pop-up presentation on a topic that is being discussed can bring about enough adrenaline and healthy pressure to complete the task.

Unhealthy Acute Stress:
Sitting in class and receiving a text that the person you have been dating for three years was just in a car accident can put the brain of an academically and emotionally sound college student under acute stress that causes a negative emotional response.

Chronic Stress

- Prolonged period of time
- Constant

While acute stress is one of the least damaging types of stress, repeated instances of it can take a toll on the body and brain. With repeated occurrence, acute stress can become chronic stress. Chronic stress is like the agitating sound of the slow drip of water from a leaky sink faucet while one is trying to sleep. Poverty is an example of chronic stress. Because scarcity captures the mind, a student's cognitive capacity is reduced when struggling to survive. Due to the high cost of higher education, students who come from families with minimal resources often experience stress as they aim to improve their lives. A student with limited resources while enrolled in school, taking 12 credit hours while working full-time (or even part-time), is most likely to experience chronic stress. The student who has a family member at home dealing with a terminal disease, substance addiction, or mental health diagnosis may be experiencing chronic stress. Prolonged amounts of stress have a direct effect on the immune system. The immune system, and its ability to destroy invading viruses and bacteria, is related to the large number of students sick in bed during and after exam time. By the end of the semester, many students describe themselves as feeling sick and tired.

Psychological Stress

Psychological/psy·cho·lo·gi·cal/(saɪkəˈlaːdʒɪkl): of, affecting, or arising in the mind; related to the mental and emotional state of a person.

- Can come with a thought or an event
- Sudden or constant
- Temporary or long term

For some students, psychological stress, the stress that comes from the way one thinks about a situation, can hit harder than any other. This form of stress can be most taxing because it is not always based on an external situation like acute and chronic stress. Stress that is psychological is energized by the person's thoughts and how they perceive things to be. Cognitive dissonance is an example of psychological stress. Cognitive dissonance, the clashing of two differing beliefs, values, or attitudes, can create a mental discomfort. In the process of learning new information, it is likely that a student will come across some information that conflicts with a long-standing belief. Based on the student's emotional awareness and emotional wealth, they can choose where the mind needs to go with their experience and perception. A student's perception, especially perceptions of threat, can affect, influence, and create the onset and passage of stress, trauma, and dis-ease in the mind and body.

A STUDENT'S VOICE

I truly appreciate the mindfulness activities I have learned. They allowed me to find a presence in a stressful moment. Mindfulness gave me time to breathe when I felt overwhelmed with challenges in my life. Mindfulness activities helped me connect to myself. I have to admit there is a lot of anger I have been carrying since 2017. I blame everything on that year. However, this class has allowed me to understand I cannot let that control me. I now have an understanding we are all given different storms because we have to do what is best and enough for ourselves. Mindfulness has taught me to breathe, listen, and connect to myself.

—An undergraduate student

STRESS AND THE BODY—FIGHT, FLIGHT, FREEZE, FAINT/FAWN

Every part of the body is the mind expressing itself through that part.

(Deb Shapiro, 2007)

When experiencing stress, the brain becomes our bodyguard. As soon as we think a thought or experience a stressor, our body is ready to respond. As our bodyguard, the brain facilitates the activation of hormones (our bodies' chemical messengers) within the body to prepare our systems to evade or confront danger. The stress response in the brain is activated and we move into the fight, flight freeze, or faint/fawn (FFFF) mode. Once in FFFF, our nervous systems go into a state of hyperarousal. A response of the sympathetic nervous system within the autonomic nervous system. When under stress, we can thank our autonomic nervous system within the reptilian brain for sounding the "fire alarm." The FFFF is here to help us survive.

Hyperarousal/hy·per·arou·sal/(-ah-rou'z'l) is a state of increased psychological and physiological tension marked by such effects as reduced pain tolerance, anxiety, exaggeration of startle responses, insomnia, fatigue, and accentuation of personality traits.

Sympathetic/sym·pa·thet·ic/(sĭm-pə-θĕt-ĭk) nervous system serves to accelerate heart rate and respiration, raise blood pressure. Release of blood sugar, adrenaline and cortisol. Fight or Flight

Autonomic/au·to·nom·ic/(ɑː.t̬ə.nɑː.mɪk) nervous system is an extensive network of neurons for regulation of the body's involuntary processes like breathing, digestion, and beating of the heart. It consists of sympathetic nervous system (SNS) and parasympathetic nervous system (PNS).

Parasympathetic/par·a·sym·pa·thet·ic/(per.ə.sĭm.pə'θĕt̬.ĭk) nervous system facilitates rest and relaxation. It helps to lower body temperature, blood pressure, heart rate, and respiration levels.

The stress response relies on two key hormones (chemical messengers)—adrenaline and cortisol—often called *stress hormones.*

Adrenaline/ Epinephrine	*Adrenaline/epinephrine is a hormone released into the bloodstream to help the body react more quickly. When stress, excitement, danger, or threat is perceived by the brain's amygdala, it sends signals to the hypothalamus that then cause the release of adrenaline into the bloodstream. Initial surges of adrenaline can create a "feel good" effect. Adrenaline works in the short term to relax airways, opening them up to take in more oxygen; increase blood sugar for more energy; increase blood flow to muscles for maximum speed and strength; and dilate pupils to enhance vision.*

(Continued)

54

Cortisol   *Cortisol is a stress hormone that is secreted into the bloodstream when the levels of adrenaline start coming down. It stimulates the amygdala and inhibits the hippocampus — it works in the long term. It builds up slowly and takes a longer time to go back to normal. Cortisol helps the body deal with stress by mobilizing resources. It also suppresses the immune system to reduce inflammation from wounds. Too much cortisol can damage the brain and body, even killing brain neurons.*

A student might describe having an "adrenaline rush" which makes them aware of noticeable symptoms like rapid heartbeat, goosebumps on the skin, and sweaty palms. Believe it or not, this physiological response is often sought out by students in their daily activities.

Physiological / phy·si·o·lo·gi·cal / (fɪziə'lɑːdʒɪkl): of or relating to the functions of living organisms and their parts.

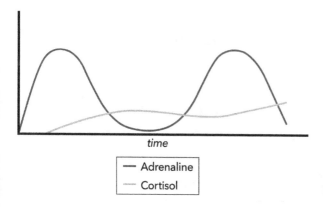

time

— Adrenaline
---- Cortisol

Stress is a relationship between you—a living, breathing organism—and the forces of the world. When a student is feeling "stressed," they physically lose connection to self. Their internal systems become dysregulated, which can in turn create dis-ease and sickness. Stress has a way to disrupt each system in the body (Parker, 2020). The short, erratic breath of a stressed respiratory system can lead to asthma and related issues. Stomach ulcers are a form of stress showing up in the stomach and digestive system. A constantly hyperactivated nervous system leads to heart and lung disease. No part of a student's body is off limits when stress is involved.

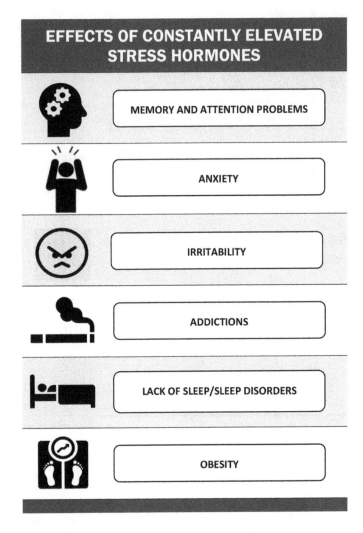

Stress changes not only how a student thinks, but also their capacity to think. They begin to see and feel the world, their relationships, and themselves in a fundamentally different way. The emotional system in their bodies changes. Imagination and the capacity to play are lost when under stress. Without imagination, the student is not able to create, solve problems, or explore options, and they lose touch with the truth of their emotions. Prolonged stress can push a student into a mood of anxiety and/or depression.

TAKE A MOMENT

Take a brief moment and ask yourself or others the following questions.

- Am I more inclined to ignore my stress so that I can continue to push through and make progress on my daily tasks and goals? If so, why?
- What small steps can I take to bring more mindfulness into my life over the next week or month? Which mindfulness practices are you most likely to use regularly? Why?
- What are the cues I can identify when I am stressed? What are my red flags that I am experiencing a chronic level of stress?
- If you could plan a low-stress, cost-effective, one-day holiday, what would it be?
- What "push" would it take for me to pause and practice stress-reduction?

Emotion/e·mo·tion/(i-'mō-shən): state that usually lasts a few seconds

Mood/mood/(müd): a feeling that persist and remains consistent over minutes/hours/days

EMOTIONS, MOOD, STRESS, AND THE BODY

Your body does not speak in English or a modern language; the language of soma is sensation. (Ruby Gibson, 2008)

There is a common thought that the mind and body are two systems that work together but function independently. However, every thought and feeling shows up in every cell of our bodies (Fleche, 2008). When an event occurs, the five senses (i.e., smell, taste, sight, sound, and touch) perceive the event. A student's "bodyguard" brain makes meaning or associates meaning to the event. The student then takes this meaning and gives it direction (energy). This is where the e-motion (energy in motion) shows up. E-motion is energy in motion (Chiasson, 2013). The type of meaning (belief) or association the student makes will determine the direction of the e-motion (energy in motion). For example, a female student is jogging across campus and she notices that an unknown male jogger is attempting to get her attention. The type of meaning (belief) she gives this event will determine the direction of her e-motion. If she chooses to associate the unknown male jogger with danger, the e-motion of fear will arise in her body.

However, if she chooses to pause and take notice of his communication, she will be able to receive the safe message that she dropped something and this is his attempt to inform her. Ultimately, the female student's brain will perceive this event through the lenses of past experiences, narratives, or images in her life.

Just like the brain is the bodyguard, emotions are our body's wisdom. They are our native language, and inherent in our emotions is wisdom. As humans, students get to practice a full range of emotions; it is healthy and critical to their wellness. Emotions come to help students deal with life's joys and challenges. The most important thing is that the emotions are felt. Below is a short, but not exhaustive, list of common emotions that come to tell students about their lives.

Common Emotions and What They Come to Tell Us (McLaren, 2020)

Anger	Anger helps us to set boundaries. It reminds us of our personal boundaries, identity, and position of boundaries. To avoid anger is to give up your position. Anger is concerned with justice, not only for yourself but for others, and especially for those who are stripped of their rights or sense of self.
Anxiety	Anxiety encourages us to slow down thoughts about the future. In order to do so, the here and now need to be attended to, one step at a time.
Fear	Fear shows up as a beautiful aspect of our body wisdom and our bodyguard brain. Fear is a strong emotion passed down from our ancestors on the Serengeti. We use fear to know when to take action or avoid harm.
Grief	Different from sadness, grief comes when you have no choice but to let go. It is a loss outside of your control of a person, a thing, or an idea.
Guilt/Shame	Guilt and shame come as a reminder not to hurt, embarrass, or dehumanize yourself or those around you.

(Continued)

Happiness	Happiness is based on happenings. It invites you to look around and appreciate all the good happenings in your life.
Joy	Joy is longstanding and long term. It comes to allow the bliss of life to be with and sit with you.
Sadness	Sadness helps us to let go of things that no longer serve us. When we let go, we can relax. We often think sadness is about loss, but it is also about a rejuvenation that creates space to welcome new things.

When a student does not allow their "self" to experience or feel an emotion, it can get locked or blocked in the body. Undesired emotions can get locked and desired emotions might get blocked. Since e-motion is energy in motion, the energy that came in needs to move through and be expressed. If not, there is an energy imbalance and then pain, stress, and/or illness come. When emotions show up, we can and should listen. The student should be encouraged to listen. Chapter 4 includes a collection of mindfulness activities that allow students brief moments with their emotions. These can be practiced once a day or several times a day. In Chapter 6, we will further discuss how to mindfully move emotions through the body.

Joy/Love/Ecstasy
warmth, expansion in
upper chest

Shame
hot sensation in face

Grief
heaviness in chest

Panic/Anxiety
sinking feeling
in stomach

Anger/Rage/Stress
tight sense in chest
or abdomen

Imbalance/Fear/Sadness
tightness or pain in the
hips

Guilt/Loneliness
lower back pain

Ego/Inability to bend
knee pain

Ungrounded
pain in the feet

59

Key to a student's optimal learning is to keep their "self" physically healthy and well rested and understand how to be aware of and regulate their e-motions (emotionally skilled). When students obtain a balanced level of physical and emotional well-being, they can then approach learning in a calm and regulated way, and do so with positive emotions. Higher education professionals can encourage students to practice expressing emotions to become more aware of their mind, body, and spirit. For example, at any time in their day of learning, the student can check in with their emotions briefly to feel what they are experiencing. If what they are feeling is perceived as good, then they should take time to enjoy that moment and consider how a good emotional state affects their thinking. If what they are feeling is uncomfortable, they can take it as a message or their body's wisdom coming to inform them. If these uncomfortable emotions are ignored, students can become restricted in how they process and respond to their environment. Brain basics knowledge coupled with e-motion body wisdom can facilitate an improved emotional and mental state. In all, by teaching students strategies that bring awareness to emotional wisdom and thought patterns, higher educational professionals are inevitably supporting students in their most vulnerable moments of coping and adapting.

When stress becomes overwhelming for students, they can practice stress-relieving activities that can calm their mind and body. Outlined below are relax and release activities, for an individual or group, that can be used to activate the body's natural relaxation response.

RELAX AND RELEASE ACTIVITIES: PRACTICE AND INTENTION

Awareness Walk

Intention: To activate the relaxation response.

- Take students to a place outdoors that is quiet.
- The goal of this awareness walk is to observe and notice.
- Have students notice what their eyes see, the smell of the air, how they feel, what they are drawn to, and what creates a feeling of joy in their body.
- Do this activity in silence for 5 minutes.

Breath Hugs

Intention: To calm our brains and bodies and practice deep breathing.

- Students are to close their eyes or gaze at the floor.
- Students take a nice, slow breath in through the nose to the count of four.

- Students exhale slowly through the mouth, like blowing a bubble, to the count of eight.
- Students relax and breathe normally.
- Have students slowly open their eyes while taking arms and stretching them out wide, relaxing shoulders, and lengthening spine.
- With arms stretched out wide, students take a nice, slow breath through the nose to the count of four.
- Students exhale slowly through the mouth, bringing arms in slowly to a count of eight and giving self a breath hug.
- Students inhale again, opening arms wide with a nice slow breath to a count of four.
- On next exhale, alternate arm that is on top, slowly hug self, and exhale to a count of eight.
- Repeat.

Breathing Ball

Intention: To learn a strategy that calms our brains and bodies and practice deep breathing.

- Hold hands out front as if holding a medium-size ball. Now bring the fingertips together as if the ball deflated.
- Students will match their breath to the movement of the ball. With each inhale, separate fingertips as if the ball is inflating. Exhale and bring fingertips back together as if the ball is deflating.
- The goal is to bring the air all the way from the nose down into the belly, practicing a deep inhale and exhale through the nose.
- Facilitator or students can decide how many breaths to take (usually between 5 and 10).

Cheek to Heart

Intention: To learn a strategy that calms our brains and bodies and connects us to the ventral vagal state. Ventral vagal is the nervous system state where we have a regulated heartbeat and are able to take full, deep breaths, keeping the nervous system in a state of safety.

- Have students place their left hand on their cheek and their right hand on their heart.
- Inform them that they are connecting with their ventral vagal state. According to Polyvagal theory, described as a useful way to understand our nervous system, the ventral vagal state is one of safety. Ventral vagal is

61

the nervous system state where we have a regulated heartbeat and are able to take full, deep breaths.

- While holding this position, students can take three deep breaths, listen to a mindfulness reading from Chapter 4, or sit in silence.

Elephant Breath

Intention: To invite playfulness back to the body and release stress from the body.

- Students take two or three steps with one foot out to the side.
- Students bend knees, lower their upper body towards the floor, bending at the hips and clasping hands together, allowing arms to dangle, like an elephant's trunk.
- The facilitator counts 3, 2, 1, and on 1, students take a big inhale, as they raise their arms above their head, hands still clasped together.
- On the exhale, students release their hands (still clasped together), swaying their trunk from up above their head to between their legs.
- Repeat three times.

Elephant Walk

Intention: To invite playfulness back to the body and release stress from the body.

- Students inhale and lift the right knee high, like an elephant preparing to march; then they exhale and stomp their foot down to the ground (it can be a big stomp if the environment allows).
- On the next inhale, have students lift the left knee high and exhale, stomping left foot down to the ground.
- For the next 10 steps, have students move in this manner on an elephant march.
- Students can stay in one place or go in any direction around the room.

Five-Finger Breathing

Intention: To learn strategies that calm our brains and bodies and practice deep breathing.

- Students make a five with the right hand and place the index finger of their left hand to the base of their right-hand thumb.
- Students use their index finger to trace each finger (between each), starting by moving the index finger up the thumb on the inhale, and as the index finger traces down the thumb, students exhale.
- Repeat until all fingers have been traced, while breathing.

Hand to Heart

Intention: To learn a strategy that calms our brains and bodies and to practice softening and gratitude.

- Have students place right hand on heart and left hand on top.
- Students, if comfortable, can close their eyes or let gaze fall to their lap.

Listen to a mindfulness reading from Chapter 4, a meaningful song, or sit in silence, activating the softening, primal feelings from the heart.

Head on Desk

Intention: To learn a strategy that calms our brains and bodies, practicing relaxing and stillness.

- Have students stack two fists with one on top of the other, either left fist glued on right fist or right fist glued on left fist.
- Students place forehead on stacked fists and glue fists to the table.
- Listen to a mindfulness reading from Chapter 4 or sit in silence, activating the calming spot between the eyes.

Left Brain/Right Brain Breath

Intention: To learn a strategy that calms our brains and bodies, tap into both hemispheres of the brain, and practice deep breathing.

- Instruct students to hold right hand out front as if giving a high five. Now use left hand to fold down the pointer and middle finger of right hand.
- Students will then use the right-hand thumb to close the right nostril and use the right hand ring or pinky finger to close the left nostril. Students will alternate between the left and right nostril with each exhale. After each inhale on one side, close the nostril and then exhale on the other side and then inhale through that side.
- The facilitator informs students that inhaling through the right nostril is a gas pedal. It is connecting to the sympathetic nervous system and the left brain hemisphere. When inhaling through this channel, more blood is fed into the left brain hemisphere and left side prefrontal cortex. The sympathetic response of increasing blood circulation, heart rate, and cortisol levels also occurs.
- The facilitator informs students that inhaling through the left nostril is the "break" system. It is connecting to the parasympathetic nervous system

and the right brain hemisphere. When inhaling through this channel, more blood is fed into the right brain hemisphere and right side prefrontal cortex. The parasympathetic response of decreased blood pressure, cooling of the body, and rest and relaxation takes place.

- Allow this process to take place for at least five breath cycles.

Three Good Things in Your Life Right Now

Intention: Practice identifying things that create happiness e-motions.

- Students are in groups of two (or larger).
- Student A tells Student B three good things in their life right now.
- Switch roles.

College students will experience stress at some point and to some degree during their collegiate career. The key for college students is to work towards not letting the stress dominate their lives and significantly disrupt their daily functioning. The downside to prolonged stress is a risk to physical, emotional, and mental well-being. As higher education professionals, we can be a part of a support system to assist students in reducing stress and enhancing their well-being. Using relax and release activities with a student or a group of students is a beneficial way to help students develop moment-to-moment awareness, focus, and mindful connection.

REFERENCES

Chiasson, A. M. (2013). *Energy Healing*. Sounds True Publications.

Fink, G. (2016). Stress, definitions, mechanisms, and effects outlined: Lessons from anxiety. In G. Fink (Ed.), *Stress, Concepts, Cognition, Emotion, and Behavior: Handbook of Stress* (Vol. 1, pp. 3–11). Elsevier.

Fleche, C. (2008). *The Biogenealogy Sourcebook. Healing the Body by Resolving Traumas of the Past*. Healing Arts Press.

Gibson, D. (2008). *My Body, My Earth. The Practice of Somatic Archeology*. iUniverse Publications.

McLaren, D. (2020). *Embracing Anxiety. How to Access the Genius of This Vital Emotion*. Sounds True Publications.

Parker, G. (2020). *Restorative Yoga for Ethnic and Race-Based Stress and Trauma*. Singing Dragon Publications.

Shapiro, D. (2007). *Your Body Speaks Your Mind. Understanding How Your Emotions and Thoughts Affect You Physically*. Sounds True Publications.

Chapter 4

A Meditation a Day

Meditation: the awareness of *no-thing*, the process of helping the mind be rather than simply think.
Mindfulness: the awareness of *some-thing*, paying attention on purpose in whatever you're doing.

Mindfulness is a process of being fully present in the moment, suspended from judgment or correction and starting with a simple awareness of one's body and thoughts (Kabat-Zinn, 2003), without attachment to a particular point of view, resulting in freedom from automatic, habitual views of the self and others (Martin, 1997). Essentially, you are paying attention on purpose in whatever you are doing. Mindfulness can be promoted through formal (e.g., meditation or yoga) or informal practice (e.g., noticing the natural landscape while on a walk). In practice, mindfulness training can provide an individual with opportunities to develop tools for cultivating internal skills such as empathy and self-efficacy; increasing awareness of their internal thoughts and feelings; remaining nonjudgmental; focusing on the present moment; using coping skills when faced with stressful situations; and managing stressful and anxiety-provoking situations (Baer, 2003; Greason & Cashwell, 2009; McKay, Wood, & Brantley, 2007). Mindfulness practice gently counters the mind's inherent need to evaluate experiences as positive or negative. Instead, the mind begins to observe experiences with an attitude of curiosity and suspended judgment, and without worry about the future or regret about the past.

With many of our lives being filled with busy schedules, it is easy to get caught up in our thoughts, emotions, and list of things to do. Our minds wander often—reflecting on what has happened, what could have been, and what could be. With such competing thoughts, it can sometimes be difficult to focus on the present. Engaging in mindfulness meditation, as a mental training practice, one can assist in slowing down such thoughts, eliminating negative thoughts, and calming both the mind and body. Other benefits that are linked to meditation include reducing stress and anxiety, increasing positive thinking, enhancing self-awareness, strengthening attention, improving memory, increasing self-control, improving sleep, reducing the arousal state, decreasing blood pressure, and regulating the function of autonomic nervous system (Fraser, 2013; National Center for Complementary and Integrative Health, n.d.). Meditation also induces physiological changes such as oxygen consumption, heart rate, respiratory amplitude and rate, skin conductance, and heart rate. Meditation helps the mind simply "be" rather than "think."

Our culture is one that conspires more towards the rational self than the intuitive self. Meditation and mindfulness deepen one's connection to self. With both, we can take time to remember that our bodies are the containers for our spirit. It is a call to respect ourselves enough to sit with "self" to better sit with all beings, with our humanity. Meditation and mindfulness are key to self-understanding, which in turn helps a student better understand the world and their "self" in the world. In addition, practicing mindfulness and meditation can be used as a part of an integrative approach for college students' well-being and wellness routine. Meditation and mindfulness invite a student's respect for self to the forefront of their life; it brings them back to calm.

A STUDENT'S VOICE

By taking part in our quiet time and meditation, I have taken the tools I have learned with breathing and self-care and placed them into action in my own life. Because of the lessons on self-care, breathing, and centering, I am more patient, kind, understanding, and peaceful after these past few months.

—An undergraduate student

In a study conducted by Davidson et al. (2003), they found that there were changes in brain functioning as a result of participation in a Mindfulness Based Stress Reduction (MBSR) program that included meditation practice. For those participants, there was significantly more activity in the left prefrontal cortex of the brain, the area of the brain associated with positive emotions and coping more effectively with stress. Furthermore, evidence shows that with mindfulness training, such as the skills associated with meditation, there is an improvement of symptoms of common mental disorders, such as anxiety and depression (Goyal et al., 2014). Therefore, mindfulness meditation can serve as a useful approach to help college students with stress and anxiety reduction and self-regulation enhancement. There are numerous styles of meditations out there—some have you watch the breath, feel the body, repeat a certain word or phrase, or create mental visualizations—but it is all a matter of finding the types that work best for each individual.

QUESTIONS FOR THE CURIOUS MINDS

How should I meditate?
The goal of meditating is to allow space for your meditation intention. It is a practice that takes practice. You might notice it a challenge at first to sit in stillness for 30 seconds or longer. It's okay. If your mind begins to wander, use the breath as a tether, send your attention to your breath, and gently pull your mind back to the moment. You can also begin to notice sounds, body sensations, or anything you choose.

What is the best way to practice mindfulness?
Mindfulness and meditation can be practiced alone, anytime, with a group or with nature. The type of practice employed is not as important as the dedication and frequency. There are plenty of websites, apps and YouTube channels that offer free mindfulness activities.

Should I practice meditation every day?
As the saying goes, practice makes perfect. It is a practice, and as with any practice, it is most beneficial and impactful when done daily. A mindfulness/meditation regime is an individual choice that can be constant or changing.

TYPES OF MEDITATION

There are different types of meditation, and it is the choice of the individual as to which way to meditate. Each individual should choose the type that meets their needs, makes them feel comfortable, and complements their disposition.

Loving Kindness (metta)	Practice to cultivate compassion, kindness, and warmth. The most common practice includes a script of traditional phrases, or you can choose one yourself. They can be repeated as thoughts or aloud several times.
Resting Awareness	Practice is an invitation to be a human being instead of human doing. It is simply noticing.
Vipassana	Practice to purify the mind, to intensely examine self, and to concentrate on self to gain insight of self. There is an invitation of existential thoughts to the mind, such as "what is suffering."
Sound Bath	Practice of bathing in ambient sound from bowls, chimes, tuning forks, gongs, or drums.
Walking	Meditation in action with walking as the focus. The practice can be done at different speeds and is encouraged to be done on varied terrains.
Chakra	Practice to seven energy centers in the body with intent to unblock or clear those areas. There are seven chakras that run down the body's midline, and each area is considered to be connected to a different body organ and gland.
Body Scan/ Progressive Relaxation	Practice of using the breath to mentally scan muscles and areas of the body to release tension or to build relationship with body parts.
Transcendental/ Mantras	Practice of seeking states, inner peace, and calm through repeating special word or phrases (mantras).

Breath is Key

Breath is life. The breath is our life force. When we connect to breath, we connect to life itself. The breath interacts with and affects every system in our body—the cardiovascular, neurological, gastrointestinal, muscular and every other system are all impacted by breathing patterns and the flow of respiration. Breathing patterns have such a profound effect on our general health as well as mental well-being. Often, symptoms of stress, disease, fear, and anxiety can lead to unhealthy breathing habits. Likewise, a constricted, rapid, jerky, or high-in the-chest breath can incite feelings of fear and activate the FFFF response, resulting in anxiety and chronic overstimulation of the sympathetic nervous system. By contrast, the intentional act of a mindful and deep diaphragm breath that moves up through the abdomen and then the chest and leaves through the nose, reflects a calm nervous system and turns on a healthy immune system. Controlling the breath helps to control the mind, heart rate, and blood pressure. How we breathe influences the size and function of the lungs.

Correlations between breathing and the state of mind and body have been made for thousands of years (Parker, 2020). In a study investigating emotional feelings and breath work, it was found that generating the emotions of joy, anger, fear, and sadness produced distinct breathing patterns. The subsequent reproduction of these distinct breathing patterns reproduced the same emotions (Philippot, Chapelle, & Blairy, 2002). Similar evidence was found in a six-month study with socially and emotionally traumatized adolescent girls in which after six months of yogic (mindful) breath work, participants' breathing rate and irregularity of breathing was reduced (Telles et al., 1997). In a study of competitive swimmers, mindful and intentional breathing practices have been shown to improve respiratory muscle endurance and decrease airway resistance and the number of strokes per breath, as well as reduce anxiety (Villate, 2015).

Breathing can be a powerful medicine. Students can use breathing to help them de-stress and calm their thoughts. Through breath work, students can learn to slow their nervous systems, develop self-control, and connect with their bodies and feelings. Higher education professionals can be a part of restoring their students' emotional health by using simple breath work and mindfulness/meditation practices. Even when not sitting in an intentional practice, it is important in your daily breath life to follow these five steps, with particular focus on the last two.

1. Become aware of your breathing pattern.
2. Breathe through your nose (mouth closed).
3. Relax. Make sure the abdominal muscles are not overly tense.
4. Slow the breath cycle, particularly the exhalation.
5. Pause at the end of each inhalation and exhalation.

A STUDENT'S VOICE

With this generation of college students, there are times when all of us feel a day full of stress or just a bad day in general ahead of us. But coming in every morning learning how to breathe, listen, meditate, and understand ourselves better takes our minds off of the day and helps us focus on the now. And even after engaging in mindfulness activities, we leave with a sense of refreshment and a little bit more clarity that helps us get through the day/week/life, reminding us how we were created to show up in life.

—An undergraduate student

A MEDITATION A DAY—31 DAYS

The following meditations can be used with a group of students or with an individual. It can be shared orally or can be given to students to practice on their own. Several of the meditations start with a small reflection that can be read aloud before going into the quiet meditation or it can be passed over. The meditations are opportunities to facilitate students' art of introspection. They allow students to dive below the surface of the mind and have reflective moments with themselves. After each activity, invite students to discuss, write, or draw what they noticed, sensed, or felt during the practice. Allow your use of these meditations to be easy, open, and flexible.

BREATH PRACTICE

How you're breathing is how you're living. (Dana Smith, 2014)

Grounding Breath

What do you think of when you hear the word "grounded"? While some of us will say "grounded" means feeling calm and centered, others recall the word as a form of punishment from their childhood. What if we acknowledge the act of our parents "grounding" us as support instead of a punishment? Let's consider some parents "grounding" intervention as a call to come back to ourselves. Perhaps our actions and the way we have been showing up is not who our parents know us to be. When we are grounded, we are better able to see who we are and were created to be. Thank goodness for our parents' assistance. Grounding is about strengthening our connection to the earth and the rich energy of the earth. It centers us.

Grounding Breath Script

Find a comfortable seat. Invite a long spine and relaxed shoulders to your body. Place hands with palms facing down on knees or at the middle of the thigh. Allow the eyes to gently close or let your gaze fall to your lap. If seated in a chair, begin to notice the placement of your feet on the earth. If sitting in a cross-legged seated position, notice the spaces where your legs, thighs, and bottom are making contact with the earth. Notice your breath. Begin a nice, easy, and slow breath in through the nose. However, on the exhale, gently bring the teeth together and exhale through the teeth and mouth, creating a calming sound of "shhhhhhh." Let's do this together again. Inhale through the nose, pause, and then with this exhale try to lengthen it out, allowing for a feeling of being more grounded and centered. Pause. Inhale through the nose. Pause. Exhale through the teeth long, slow, and deep.

Repeat this process for a total of between three and five times, or as often as needed. Invite the student's or students' attention back to the moment by a gentle movement of their hands and feet and by opening their eyes.

Collective Breath

Research has shown that when we sing together, our hearts begin to beat together. Can we consider the same thing to be true for when we breathe together—that our hearts begin to beat together? When singing, there is a breathing pattern that becomes coordinated amongst all involved. Once the inhale is complete and the exhale starts, there is an activation of the vagus nerve (the nerve that connects the brain and heart). With the collective inhale and exhale comes the public kinship. With the slight pause in between, we get to experience a kindred pause. It is just like in our lives when we pause for an emergency vehicle. You can feel a moment of stillness that offers all involved a public kinship, a collective moment of stillness.

Collective Breath Script

Find a comfortable seat. Invite a long spine and relaxed shoulders to your body. Place your hands on the belly or let them rest on your lap. Begin to gently close your eyes or let the gaze fall to your lap. Begin to notice your breath. Notice your natural breath cycle. Notice the inhale and where it begins. Notice the exhale and where it lands. Can you notice the gentle lift of your body as you inhale and settle down as you exhale? Can you notice the slight pause in between? We will begin a collective breath together to a four/six count. That means when we inhale through the nose, it will be to a four count, and we will exhale through the nose to a six count. Let's begin. Inhale—ohm one—ohm two—ohm three— ohm four. Pause. Exhale—ohm one—ohm two—ohm three—ohm four—ohm five—ohm six. Pause.

Repeat two or three more times. Invite the student's or students' attention back to the moment by a gentle movement of their hands and feet and by opening their eyes.

Sigh to Release Breath

Sigh the breath out so we can get down to what is real. Life is real. In order to get to life, we have to expand life. In order to expand life, we need to move—move our bodies, move our energy, move our breath. Moving the breath helps us move both physically and emotionally. It allows us to be more spacious; to move spaciously without constriction, without feeling bound. When we move, we breath. Even in our stillness we are moving—moving thoughts, moving feelings, and moving energy and answers before us. Our breath is real. The breath is also both voluntary and involuntary. It does what it needs to do to take care of us.

A sigh is a deep breath. It is not usually a voluntary breath. It usually happens when the body says so. It is a healthy way to release psychological tension. It starts out as a normal breath, but before you exhale, you take a second breath on top of it. With the exhale, a beautiful release and relief take place. The relief is the result of a sudden change in respiratory patterns. Since the sigh is a part of our body's regular breathing pattern, when we do a really good one effectively, we access our stress coping reserves. When we sigh it out, we are releasing, we down-regulate our bodies, and we bring back focus. Sighing can bring us back home to ourselves.

Sigh to Release Script

Find a comfortable seat. Invite a long spine and relaxed shoulders to your body. Place hands with palms facing up or down on knees or at the middle of the thigh. Allow the eyes to gently close or let your gaze fall to your lap. Begin to notice your breath. Invite an easy inhale and then after a pause, open the mouth for a small force of air and loud sigh.

Repeat this process three or four times or when the body says stop. Invite the student's or students' attention back to the moment by a gentle movement of their hands and feet and by opening their eyes.

Uplift Breath

It has been said that the best way to uplift our own life is to uplift that of others. Our breath, coupled with intention, can be used to offer well wishes to others and even ourselves.

Uplift Breath Script

Find a comfortable seat. Invite a long spine and relaxed shoulders to your body. Bring palms together (peace offering/prayer hands) in front of the heart. Allow the eyes to stay open or gently close. As you inhale, raise the arms above the head with palms together. Pause at the top. Exhale while opening the hands and arms wide and releasing down as if a volcano erupting or creating a rainbow above. Bring hands back together at the heart. Now, set an intention for the next one. With your hands together at the heart, bring someone to your mind that could use a little extra love, healing, or support. As you lift your hands, send into the air some extra love, kindness, or healing that person may need. Slowly spread the arms out as if that love is leaving from the tips of each of your fingers. Bring your palms back together at the heart.

Repeat as often as desired with a person and intention in mind, or imagine that you are covering yourself with just what you need. Invite the student's or students' attention back to the moment by a gentle movement of their hands and feet and by opening their eyes.

Ocean Breath/Victorious Breath

There is a breath practice in yoga that sounds very similar to the sound of Darth Vader breathing. It creates a sound in the back of throat while also giving a massage to the back of the throat. This in turn creates a calming and balancing feeling over your body. It is most often used when in movement in yoga, in practice with gentle movement.

Ocean Breath Script

Find a comfortable position in your chair or seated cross-legged. With eyes still open, begin to notice your breath. Quietly say the word "whisper" a few times. As you do, notice the movement of air on the back of the throat. Now on the next "whisper," gently bring the lips together and keep saying whisper and hold it longer at the end. With the lips together, inhale through the nose and immediately follow with "whisper." See if you can lengthen the exhale each time. Let's do that two more times. Now, let's add some movement to it. On the inhale, take arms wide and up to the sky. Pause at the top. On the "whisper," exhale, take arms wide, then back down.

Repeat this process with movement between three and five more times. Invite the student's or students' attention back to the moment by a gentle movement of their hands and feet and by opening their eyes.

Three-Part Breath

The breath is our anchor. The breath reminds us to be where our feet are, to be here now, because we cannot breathe in the future nor in the past. How we are breathing is a reflection of how we are living. Three-part breath is an intentional deepening of the breath and relaxing of muscles to calm the body. It is an excellent practice when feeling stressed or when your breath feels constricted.

Three-Part Breath Script

Come to a comfortable position in a chair or on the floor. Roll the shoulders back and down as you lengthen the spine. Soften your heart and shoulders. Gently close your eyes or let the gaze fall to your lap. Place one hand on your belly and take one deep slow breath into the belly. Feel the belly inflate like a balloon and deflate as you exhale. Practice this two more times. Move your hand to the bottom of the sternum. On the next inhale, notice the ribs expand laterally and retract on the exhale. Practice this two more times. Now place your hand below the collarbone at the center of your chest and inhale. Feel the chest open up as you inhale and withdraw with the exhale. Practice this for two more breaths. Now bring it all together. On the next inhale, start at the belly, move to the lower sternum, and then to the upper chest area. Pause. Surrender into the exhale in reverse, chest, lower sternum, and belly.

Repeat this process two or three more times. Invite the students' or students' attention back to the moment by a gentle movement of their hands and feet and by opening their eyes.

Hover Breath

If you are breathing, you are amazing. The following breath activity is to show you that there are as many ways to breathe as there are foods to eat. In this practice, we take a new breath as we take tiny sip inhales and one squeeze out on the exhale (i.e., a hover breath).

Hover Breath Script

Come to a comfortable position in a chair or on the floor. Roll the shoulders back and down as you lengthen the spine. Soften your heart and shoulders. Gently close your eyes or let your gaze fall to your lap. Begin to notice your natural breath cycle. With the next inhale, invite four tiny sips that are just enough to get a complete inhale, pause, and then exhale it out. Now, focus on the bottom of the exhale and the point where you feel like all the breath is out of the body. Pause, and then squeeze from the space below the belly button to push out any last pieces of air. Now enjoy one full natural inhale and exhale.

Repeat this process three or four times. Invite the student's or students' attention back to the moment by a gentle movement of their hands and feet and by opening their eyes.

HEALTHY BREATH CHEAT SHEET

(Adapted FROM Nestor, 2020)

- The breath is the only physiological function controlled by both the voluntary and involuntary system.
- Most of us breathe too much. We have become a culture of over-breathers. Just like society's pace, our breath is fast-paced, short, and erratic. Breathing just 10 percent more than the body needs can overwork our systems.
- In one single breath, more molecules of air pass through your nose than all the sand on all the beaches of the world. In each breath, we experience an absorbing of ourselves in what surrounds us. With each exhale, we give pieces of us back out. Respiration is reciprocation.
- Each inhale we take provides us with new energy, and each exhale releases old, stale energy from our bodies. The breath allows us to hack into our nervous system, control our immune system, and restore our health.
- Mouth breathing changes our physical bodies and our airways for the worse. The tissue in the back of the throat becomes loose and flexes inward, making breathing more difficult. It causes the body to lose 40 percent more water.
- Nose breathing is best. It clears air, heats it, and moistens it for easier absorption. It forces air against the tissues in the back of the throat, making the airways wider and breathing easier.
- Our ancestors knew the breath as a powerful medicine, a force. It has been called the "great secret of life." They practiced methods to train children to breathe through their nose, a habit they would carry the rest of their lives.

INTENTIONS PRACTICE
Intention of Balance

Let's allow ourselves to think about the word "intention." Intention is about how you choose to show up. It is about the here and now. Through our intentions, we all have the ability to choose how we will show up in the here and now. Let's use this time to set an intention of balance—balanced energy in our bodies. Pause for a few seconds of reflective silence. Because we live in a culture that conspires towards the rational, and we carry the bulk of our energy in our heads, not our bodies, we are often imbalanced. We stay "worked up," hurried, and anxious. We pull the energy of pain, trauma, and trouble to our heads. We tend to overthink things in an attempt to solve them. Doing so causes our energy and "e-motions" to rise up. Keeping this energy centered upward can lead to an imbalance of the nervous system and create an overactive sympathetic nervous system.

Intention of Balance Breath Script

Come to a comfortable position in a chair or on the floor. Roll the shoulders back and down as you lengthen the spine. Soften your heart and shoulders. Relax your face and forehead. Relax the tongue. Allow the whole upper body to relax and then gently close your eyes or let your gaze fall to your lap. Notice the place where your feet are on the earth. Take your mind's eye there. Imagine that with the next inhale, you are pulling rich energy from the earth into the bottom of your feet. As you continue with the exhale, invite the energy to begin to move with your breath. Keep inhaling and exhaling and now move the energy up through your shins, your calves and to your knees. Feel the kneecaps gently lift. Continue to breathe and invite the energy up your thighs and to the hips. Pause at the hips. Stay here for two full breaths and imagine that the energy is moving through the hips clearing out any congestion or blockage. With the next breath, bring the energy up through the torso and to the shoulders. Let the energy move up to the top of the crown. Once there, begin to notice the breath again and stay at the crown for two more breaths to gather up all the heavy thoughts, responsibilities, and worries that may be lingering. Once gathered, use the breath to take it all down the back side of you—just letting it all fall off your back like a waterfall. Continue to breathe with your mind's eye observing all worries fall away and off your back. Let the energy fall down until you feel a balance with the top, center, and bottom of you.

Invite the student's or students' attention back to the moment by a gentle movement of their hands and feet and by opening their eyes.

Intention Shoulders

Intention is all about how you choose to show up—how you choose to show up in your day, your life, and your relationships. As humans, we even have the capacity to set an intention of how we move in our bodies. Have you ever taken notice of how some people seem to walk and move with a natural grace and lift, while others seem heavy and strong in their movement? The way we move our bodies is also a communication of our mood and emotions. When happy, we seem to glide. When upset or sad, we seem to drag. Let's practice and notice for ourselves.

Intention Shoulders Breath Script

Come to a comfortable position in a chair or on the floor. Roll the shoulders back and down as you lengthen the spine. Soften your heart and shoulders. Relax your face and forehead. Bringing awareness to your shoulders; notice if they are tensed or relaxed. Take your right hand to the top of the left shoulder, and slide it down the arm as you think of the word "soften." Now, do the opposite. Take your left hand to the top of your right shoulder and slide it down the arm as you think of the word "soften." Keep your attention on your shoulders as you again notice your breath. On your next inhale, bring the shoulders towards the ears. Exhale and take them back down. Inhale and move the shoulders forward. Exhale, and move them back. Now we will bring intention to this movement. Gently close your eyes to help "you see." The first intention of movement in our shoulders will be that of clouds. Imagine that your two shoulders are big fluffy clouds, moving free and easy across the sky. Inhale and float your clouds up. Exhale, and float them down. Inhale, float forward and exhale, and then float back. Now relax and notice.

Repeat the same shoulder movement sequence with different intentions such as "excited shoulders" or "glide shoulders," or make up your own. Invite the student's or students' attention back to the moment by a gentle movement of their hands and feet and by opening their eyes.

Intentional Listening

This activity can be done with a chime, a bell, a hand drum, or something to bring students' attention to focus. If you so choose, you can do it without one. Attention is energizing. Intention is transforming.

Intentional Listening Breath Script

Find a comfortable seat. Invite a long spine and relaxed shoulders to your body. Place your hands on your lap or let them rest on your thighs or at the end of your

77

knees. Gently close your eyes or let your gaze fall to your lap. Notice the breath. I invite you to listen to the sound (if working with a chime, ring the chime and welcome them to listen to it). Ride the sound out until the very last second, and when you can no longer hear it, allow for a full exhale. Begin to bring your attention to your ears. Allow an intentional listening ear. As you listen, begin to notice the sounds outside of this room (pause for about 10 seconds to allow the student or students to listen). Now, let's shift that listening attention and begin to notice the sounds inside of this room (pause for about 10 seconds to allow the student or students to listen). Let's allow for one more listening journey. Place your left hand on your heart, and your right hand on top. Take a breath in and breathe out. Now listen (pause for about 10 seconds to allow students to listen). At first you may begin to notice the beating of your heart, but allow yourself to listen even deeper. Are you able to hear and feel any emotions? Your soft emotions? Perhaps you can hear a little compassion or maybe some kindness. What about forgiveness? You see, sometimes the tender emotions in our hearts tend to get drowned out by the louder, more aggressive emotions like anger, frustration, fear, and worry. Allow yourself to soften and listen for what your heart is feeling today (allow a few more seconds of stillness, and then welcome the student's or students' attention back to the moment by a gentle movement of their hands and feet and by opening their eyes).

Intentions and Goals

Come to a comfortable position in a chair or on the floor. Roll the shoulders back and down as you lengthen the spine. Soften your shoulders. Relax your face and forehead. You are welcome to gently close your eyes or let your gaze fall to your lap. Begin to notice your breath. Notice the rise and fall of the chest and belly with each inhale and exhale. Place your left hand on your heart and the right hand on top. Notice this space at the center of your chest. Notice it as your heart center, the place where your intentions reside. Allow the ears to listen. Intention is all about how you choose to show up—how you choose to show up in your day, your life, and your relationships. Intention is about the here and now. Goals are about the future. We all were taught about goals and how to set them during our K–12 experience. Goals are about outcomes and things we want to accomplish in the future. However, intention is about the here and now, and how you choose to show up. Take a few seconds with your breath and reflect on how you are choosing to show up today.

Allow a few more seconds of stillness, and then welcome the student's or students' attention back to the moment by a gentle movement of their hands and feet and by opening their eyes.

Heart Intention

Come to a comfortable position in a chair or on the floor. Roll the shoulders back and down as you lengthen the spine. Soften your shoulders. Relax your face and forehead. You are welcome to gently close your eyes or let your gaze fall to your lap. Begin to notice your breath. Notice the rise and fall of the chest and belly with each inhale and exhale. Do this—place your left hand on your heart and your right hand on top. Now soften (allow for a few seconds of silence). When we put our hands on our hearts, something awakens and we soften. It is almost as if something primal feels us and we feel it breathe into and from the heart. On the next inhale, imagine that the breath is moving into the heart. As you exhale, allow the breath to leave from this same space. With each breath, we are doing an intentional heart clearing.

Repeat these breaths eight to ten more times. Invite student's or students' attention back to the moment by a gentle movement of their hands and feet and by opening their eyes.

Intention and Power

Come to a comfortable position in a chair or on the floor. Roll the shoulders back and down as you lengthen the spine. Soften your shoulders. Relax your face and forehead. You are welcome to gently close your eyes so that you can "see," or let your gaze fall to your lap. Begin to notice your breath. Notice the rise and fall of the chest and belly with each inhale and exhale. Place your left hand on your heart and your right hand on your belly. Allow yourself to notice the rise and fall of the belly and the chest. Now, bring your mind's eye to the space behind your right hand. Notice this space as the center of you. Feel that space being strong and confident. Notice that when you feel in control, you feel it in this area. Researchers have suggested that this area, what is often called the gut, is our first brain and the location of our self-reliance. This is where we trust our inner guidance. It is where the seed of our personal power resides. Feel the energy there. It is where we go for answers when we don't need others' approval or validation. Keep breathing into this space. As you breathe, it is important to distinguish that personal power does not imply power over others. It implies self-mastering—our ability to master our thoughts and our emotions. We know that these emotions come to inform us. Inhale and exhale. Now, bring your attention and mind's eye up to the area behind your left hand. This area is where your intention resides. Your intentions are all about how you choose to show up in the here and now. Breathe into that space and notice. What would it look like if your intentions and power were lined up daily? Now sit with this question for three more breaths.

Invite the student's or students' attention back to the moment by a gentle movement of their hands and feet and by opening their eyes.

AWARENESS
When You Can't Hear the Birds

Come to a comfortable position in a chair or on the floor. Roll the shoulders back and down as you lengthen the spine. Gently close your eyes or let the gaze fall to your lap. Begin to focus your awareness on your breath. Imagine that you are outdoors in a cool open space with trees nearby. This space feels safe and welcoming. The sun has yet to rise and you can smell the cool morning air. You sit and wait to hear the first bird chirp and the sound of the dawn cracking. You have been here before and appreciate the beautiful bird songs. They often feel like songs of love and kindness just for you. When your mind is at peace, you notice that you can hear the birds so clearly. You also notice that on those mornings when you are distracted or hold something heavy on your mind, you are not able to hear the birds. No matter how hard you try to give your attention to their sweet song, your mind is so distracted and full of noise that you can't hear the birds sing. Take a moment to notice right now. Notice if you have a calm mind, one that is free, calm, and clear—a mind that is able to enjoy the song of the morning bird (give the student or students a few moments to notice). Now gently begin to bring yourself back to the room by moving your fingers, wiggling your toes, and gently opening your eyes.

As Soon as You Think a Thought, the Body Responds

Come to a comfortable position in a chair or on the floor. Roll the shoulders back and down as you lengthen the spine. Gently close your eyes or let the gaze fall to your lap. Begin to focus your awareness on your breath. Relax your thoughts and just be (offer a few seconds of silence for students to sit in stillness). The brain is a powerful tool that is here to protect us, to keep us safe. It is our bodyguard, and its sole mission is to protect us from danger and to maintain balance in our bodies. Let's think and feel the word "calm" (offer a few seconds of silence for students to sit in stillness). We will move calm through our bodies. Starting at the top of the crown, repeat in your mind "brain calm." Then move down and repeat the following in your mind—Face calm. Shoulders calm. Stomach calm. Arms calm. Hands calm. Legs calm. Knees calm. Ankles calm. Feet calm.

Repeat this as many times as you need, starting at the crown and moving to the feet.

Carry Your Stillness

Come to a comfortable position in a chair or on the floor. Roll the shoulders back and down as you lengthen the spine. Gently close your eyes or let the gaze fall to your lap. Begin to focus your awareness on your breath. Relax your thoughts and just be. Bring stillness to your body and to your thoughts by counting down slowly from ten. Let's follow this count together as you keep breathing in and out. Ten. Nine. Eight. Seven. Six. Five. Four. Three. Two. One. Relax your face, your tongue, and your jaw muscles. As you let the stillness settle in, be okay with the mind trying to wander. If it does, with a gentle pull, bring it right back to this moment by noticing the breath. As we sit here in stillness, we welcome the awareness that at any time in our day, week, or life we can come back to this place of stillness. We can actually carry our stillness with us everywhere we go. As we do, the chaos around won't overshadow the peace within. Stay here for five to ten more breaths and then gently bring your awareness back to the room by opening your eyes.

We Close Our Eyes to See

Come to a comfortable position in a chair or on the floor. Roll the shoulders back and down as you lengthen the spine. Begin to focus your awareness on your breath. Relax your thoughts. Gently close your eyes so that you can "see." By closing your eyes, you heighten your other senses and awareness. More of your energy and processing powers are shifted to your other senses and the "felt sense of you." Can you see you better? Can you see and feel any places in your body that may be aching or are joyful? With your eyes closed, are you able to feel yourself balanced in your seat? Balanced in life? As you answer these questions in your mind, take a total of six to eight full breaths in and out.

Allow the student or students a few minutes to sit with the questions before inviting them to open their eyes and return their awareness to the room.

Positivity? Negativity?

Come to a comfortable position in a chair or on the floor. Roll the shoulders back and down as you lengthen the spine. Begin to focus your awareness on your breath. Notice your thoughts. Notice that our thoughts are a force. For anything to move, you need a force behind it pushing it or on another side pulling it. What way have your thoughts, this powerful force, been moving lately? We can gather this information by bringing awareness to the conversations we have been having lately. Whether it be with a friend, family member, or work colleague, have your thoughts and words been a force of positivity or negativity? Have the words you've been sharing been positive and life giving or negative and energy draining? Do your daily conversations facilitate a life of ease? Effort? Rest? Creation? Take a breath and inhale ease, exhale challenge. Inhale balanced effort, exhale overexertion. Inhale rest, exhale overactivity. Inhale creativity, exhale stagnation.

Sit with You as a Radical Act of Sanity

Come to a comfortable position in a chair or on the floor. Roll the shoulders back and down as you lengthen the spine. Become aware of your breath. Gently drop your gaze or close your eyes. Bring both hands to the belly or the heart, whichever feels more comfortable. Right now, we get to suspend all judgment— judgment of self and judgment of others. I invite you to take up residency in this awareness. Let's drop into the awareness of the full dimensionality of the inhale. Pause. Now drop into the awareness of the full dimensionality of the exhale (allow a pause for the students to experience). Ride the waves of your own breathing (allow a pause for the students to experience). The breath helps to stabilize us in our own awareness. If the mind wanders, it's okay. The breath will take care of us. Allow this time to take up residency in awareness of your own rhythmic breathing. Breathe. Sit. Let the mind calm. Sit with "you" as a radical act of sanity. Allow this stillness for seven more breaths and then gently bring your attention back to the room.

CONNECTION

Selfless Action, Selfless Service without Any Attachment to an Outcome

Come to a comfortable position in a chair or on the floor. Roll the shoulders back and down as you lengthen the spine. Gently close your eyes or let your gaze fall to your lap. Begin to connect to your breath. Let's use our breath to connect to self, but not only self—also to others. Bring palms together at your heart. Inhale and exhale. Now recognize that this current state of breath is especially special if you are aware. Because this breath is so special, we can use the breath to bring us to selfless actions and selfless service without any attention. On your next inhale and exhale, let's direct the breath to individuals that might be weary with the challenges of life. Let's use the next breath to send peace and clarity to all of our local officials and representatives. Let's use the next breath to comfort all the mothers of the slain (pause to allow for a few more breaths). Let's use the next breath to send safety to those on the front lines of war, medical support, and educational environments. Allow the next breath to be a breath of selfless action and selfless service toward a person or people group of your choice. This type of action pours energy into all that is right with you. Allow this connection to others for seven more breaths and then gently bring your attention back to the room.

Life Wants You

Come to a comfortable position in a chair or on the floor. Roll the shoulders back and down as you lengthen the spine. Gently close your eyes or let your gaze fall to your lap. Begin to connect to your breath. Allow your inhale to flow free and easy. Allow the exhale to flow free and easy. In your mind or by whisper, connect to and repeat the following affirmations. "As long as I am breathing, I can start all over again" (pause to allow time to repeat). "The breath will take care of me" (pause to allow time to repeat). "I align myself with the best parts of me" (pause to allow time to repeat). "My breath helps to stabilize me" (pause to allow time to repeat). "A lot of answers to my questions are sitting right next to the questions" (pause to allow time to repeat). "It doesn't matter if a person or people or groups don't want me because life wants me" (allow student or students a few more moments of silence to allow for a full affirmation download). Gently begin to wiggle your fingers and your toes, returning your attention to the room and opening your eyes.

We All Came to this Earth as Love—
Creative Authority of Social Justice

Come to a comfortable position in a chair or on the floor. Roll the shoulders back and down as you lengthen the spine. Gently close your eyes or let your gaze fall to your lap. Begin to connect to your breath. Did you know that we all came to this earth as love? We were all born with an inherent wisdom in our hearts. Our hearts came filled with love, compassion, and kindness. We only know these emotions until the world begins to tell us how to fear, judge, and try to control. Right now, let's listen and feel from the wisdom of the heart. Invite a breath in and out while preparing the heart to take a few moments to visit some tough places. Let's visit with those tough spaces of judgment for others because of their skin color, socioeconomic background, religion, or sexuality. Allow yourself to even notice any feelings in your body as I said those words (give students an opportunity to notice by being silent for a few seconds). Take a breath in and then sigh it out. We can approach these tough places, the places of pain and long-time coming pain that we often push away. But the heart can endure, it can transmute all the pain to an awareness—an awareness of us, our life, and how we show up in life as it relates to judgment or oppression of others. Allow yourself to become aware of any discomfort. There is a beauty in the discomfort. We get to face what we have not been facing. Notice that when you sense your heart moving away to places of fear and anger, we have to muscle our way from the fear of the mind and sit at the door of your heart. We can sit in the quiet and stillness of our heart and close the door on fear, on ego, on racism, on classism, on sexism, on patriotism, and on homophobia. Notice your breath and allow for a shift to take place in your mind and heart. We can even shed the skin of old ways, old thoughts, and old beliefs so we don't suffocate. If you are not able to immediately see old ways that need to be changed, take a breath and then say, "show me." Allow your body to speak.

Allow a few more seconds of stillness, and then welcome the student's or students' attention back to the moment by a gentle movement of their hands and feet and by opening their eyes.

Energy. Body. Connect.

We are all energy. Our thoughts are energy. Our emotions are energy, e-motion, energy in motion. We are all electromagnetic energy, the same energy that the stars in the sky are made of. How do you take care of the energy within you? Most of the time, pain is the result of blocked energy. We all have the capacity to move blocked energy within. We can use movement, touch, sound, vibration, light, and even nature to do this. Most importantly, we can connect to the breath and use the breath to move some blocked energy that may be showing up as a pain in our body.

Energy. Body. Connect. Breath Script

Come to a comfortable position in a chair or on the floor. Roll the shoulders back and down as you lengthen the spine. Gently close your eyes or let your gaze fall to your lap. Begin to connect to your breath. Allow yourself to notice. Notice yourself noticing. Begin to notice if there are any areas of your body that may have pain, constriction, or discomfort. If so, place your hand on that area. Now connect your breath to that area. If there is no particular area that is bothering you, place your hands on your heart. Feel a healing shift being transferred through the touch of your hands. Stay connected to that location on your body, and breathe in and out of that space for seven more breath cycles.

Allow a few more seconds of stillness, and then welcome the student's or students' attention back to the moment by a gentle movement of their hands and feet and by opening their eyes.

Connect to Your Struggle

Inside our struggle, we find a way to look at pain in a different way. In our struggle, we are often humbled and transformed.

Connect to Your Struggle Breath Script

Come to a comfortable position in a chair or on the floor. Roll the shoulders back and down as you lengthen the spine. Gently close your eyes or let your gaze fall

84

to your lap. Begin to connect to your breath. As you connect to the breath, allow yourself to connect to a memory, a thought, or an experience that created struggle for you. Allow yourself to connect to the feeling it brings. Then, lovingly notice yourself sitting with this. Notice the emotion. Now, use your imagination and see yourself outside of you and notice your face. Notice your body. Inhale and exhale. Can you see you with a real close friend or child? Or maybe a loved one? Can you see yourself sitting with that friend who is in a tough place? What would you say to that friend?

Allow a few moments of silence for the student or students to explore and connect to this experience and then invite them back to the room with a wiggle of their fingers and toes and by opening their eyes.

Connect to Nature

Come to a comfortable position in a chair or on the floor. Roll the shoulders back and down as you lengthen the spine. Gently close your eyes or let your gaze fall to your lap. Begin to connect to your breath. Allow yourself to connect to your imagination. Imagine mother earth's four elements—water, fire, wind, and earth. Take two deep breaths in and out and allow yourself to connect with each. Imagine yourself standing in strong wind and feel it on your skin. Open yourself up to the movement of the energy (pause to allow student or students the experience). Imagine yourself sitting in a gentle rain and feel it on your skin. Open yourself up to the movement of the energy (pause to allow student or students the experience). Imagine yourself on the beach on a hot day with the sun shining, a nice breeze, and your body resting on the cool sand. Open yourself up to the movement of the energy (pause to allow student or students the experience). Imagine yourself sitting in a blanket on a cool fall evening next to a campfire with all of your favorite people. Open yourself up to the movement of the energy. Take a second to notice which element your body prefers.

Allow a few moments of silence for the student or students to explore and connect to this experience and then invite them back to the room with a wiggle of their fingers and toes and by opening their eyes.

REFLECTION
Name Your Day

Come to a comfortable position in a chair or on the floor. Roll the shoulders back and down as you lengthen the spine. Gently close your eyes or let your gaze fall to your lap. Begin to use the breath as a tool for reflection. Let's allow our minds to reflect for a bit. Let's reflect on the morning—the morning time when you first begin to gain consciousness. Each morning, when you wake, what is the first thought that comes to your mind? Do you immediately go into a thought of "Good morning, I'm so happy to be alive," or do you go to "I'm tired and didn't get enough sleep?" Allow the following awareness. Whatever thought you choose to start your day with is often what you name your day. If your thought is "I didn't get enough sleep," you have just named your day, "Not Enough." However, if you begin with gratitude, with thoughts such as "I am so thankful for a new day" or "I am so thankful for fresh drinking water," you name your day "gratitude." Notice your inhale and exhale. Let's allow ourselves a short time of reflection on how we commonly start our days. What do we name our day?

Allow a few more seconds of reflection, and then welcome the student's or students' attention back to the moment by a gentle movement of their hands and feet and by opening their eyes.

Your Pharmacy Within is Waiting for You to Tap into It

We all have a pharmacy within. Your pharmacy within is waiting for you to tap into it. Not only can the breath be some powerful medicine for us, but we also have some hormones within that can deliver good feelings through our bodies.

Pharmacy Within Breath Script

Come to a comfortable position in a chair or on the floor. Roll the shoulders back and down as you lengthen the spine. Gently close your eyes or let your gaze fall to your lap. Begin to use the breath as a tool for reflection. Let's take this moment to reflect on our favorite childhood snack (pause to allow student or students the experience). Let's take this moment to reflect on our favorite activity to do outdoors (pause to allow student or students the experience). Let's take this moment to reflect on three things we are grateful for (pause to allow student or students the experience). Let's take this moment to reflect on a really good hug from a grandparent, elder, or family member (pause to allow students the experience). Stay with this reflection for four more breaths and allow the body to release a few good shots of oxytocin, serotonin, and dopamine.

Allow a few more seconds of reflection, and then welcome the student or students' attention back to the moment by a gentle movement of their hands and feet and by opening their eyes.

5, 4, 3, 2, 1

Sometimes when feeling worried, anxious, or afraid, we can lose orientation with the here and now, activate the stress response, and lose our connection and location on earth. We can use a reflection of our five senses to remind us we are safe and present and to activate the relaxation response in our brains.

5, 4, 3, 2, 1 Breath Script

Come to a comfortable position in a chair or on the floor. Roll the shoulders back and down as you lengthen the spine. Gently close your eyes or let your gaze fall to your lap. Begin to use the breath as a tool for reflection. You are here now. Reflect on five songs or sounds you enjoy hearing (pause to allow the student or students the experience). Reflect on four things, animals, or people you like to see (pause to allow students the experience). Reflect on three foods you love to taste (pause to allow student or students the experience). Reflect on two scents you are grateful for (pause to allow student or students the experience). Reflect on one person you love to receive a hug from.

Allow a few more seconds of reflection, and then welcome the student's or students' attention back to the moment by a gentle movement of their hands and feet and by opening their eyes.

We Are All More Powerful than the Situations We Go Through

Come to a comfortable position in a chair or on the floor. Roll the shoulders back and down as you lengthen the spine. Gently close your eyes or let your gaze fall to your lap. Bring your hands to your belly—your power center. Begin to use the breath as a tool for reflection. Let's take this moment to reflect on all the situations you have overcome (pause to allow student or students the experience). Life is full of challenges. Yet, we are constantly rising above those challenges. The fact that you are still here is proof that you are stronger than the situations you go through. Take a breath and feel this truth in your body. Maximize your reflections of strength and times you did not fold. Maximize those best experiences in your body and mind to strengthen you (pause to allow student or students the experience). It is your choice to see the "overcome" that you have displayed in your life. Take three deep breaths in and out. Feel the strength in your body and open your eyes.

There is Far More Right with You than Wrong with You

Come to a comfortable position in a chair or on the floor. Roll the shoulders back and down as you lengthen the spine. Gently close your eyes or let your gaze fall to your lap. Bring your hands to your heart. Take this time to get out of your own way with any negative thoughts, negative self-talk, or criticism about yourself. Remember, there is far more right with you than wrong. As you inhale, inhale love for yourself and exhale sending love to others. As you inhale, call on the strong parts of you. Let this right now breathing pour energy into what's right with you. Right now, this is about your awareness, your intention, your

87

connection, and your truest nature. Who are you really? What is your truest nature? Rest in this awareness. Breathe. Sit. Notice. Listen.

Allow a few more seconds of reflection, and then welcome the student's or students' attention back to the moment by a gentle movement of their hands and feet and by opening their eyes.

Reflect and Remind *(Lillie's Reminder)*

Come to a comfortable position in a chair or on the floor. Roll the shoulders back and down as you lengthen the spine. Gently close your eyes or let your gaze fall to your lap. Bring your palms together at your heart center in gratitude/prayer hands. On your next breath, raise your hands up and pause at the middle of your forehead. We bring our hands here as a reminder of clear thoughts. With the next breath, guide your hands down, palms together, and pause before your lips. We bring our hands here as a reminder of clear speech. We speak life, not just over others but over ourselves. On the next inhale and exhale, slide your hands down, back to the front of the heart. We bring our hands here as a reminder of clear intentions. I remind you all, that each and every day as you move on this earth and dance across this world, you get to function from approval and not for approval. Because upon your creation, you were already approved. The light in me honors the light in you.

Allow a few more seconds of reflection, and then welcome the student's or students' attention back to the moment by a gentle movement of their hands and feet and by opening their eyes.

TAKE A MOMENT

Take a brief moment and ask yourself or others the following questions.

- What are my typical first thoughts when I wake in the morning?
- If I am honest with myself and take a moment to reflect on my week, what, if anything, am I taking for granted? Am I taking on a healthy perspective?
- What are my thoughts on meditation? Do I believe it is possible to change behavior unconsciously through mindfulness meditation? Why do I think this is possible?
- Am I ready to make a behavior change to pay attention on purpose?
- What else is going on in my life right now that impacts my ability to commit to practicing meditation? Considering these factors, do I have the time and energy for a practicing meditation?

- If I am really honest with myself, am I willing to commit to meditation and mindfulness practices for a set time per week?
- What is the biggest barrier that would prevent me from committing to a practice of meditation? Why?
- What is something I hope to achieve through practicing mindfulness or meditation?

REFERENCES

Baer, R. A. (2003). Mindfulness training as a clinical intervention: A conceptual and empirical review. *Clinical Psychology: Science and Practice, 10*(2), 125–143. https://doi.org/10.1093/clipsy.bpg015

Davidson, R. J., Kabat-Zinn, J., Schumacher, J., Rosenkranz, M., Muller, D., Santorelli, S. F. & Sheridan, J.F. (2003). Alterations in brain and immune function produced by mindfulness meditation. *Psychosomatic Medicine, 65*(4), 564–570. https://doi:10.1097/01.psy.0000077505.67574.e3

Fraser, A. (Ed.). (2013). *The Healing Power of Meditation: Leading Experts on Buddhism, Psychology, and Medicine Explore the Health Benefits of Contemplative Practice.* Shambhala Publications.

Goyal, M., Singh, S., Sibinga, E. M., Gould, N. F., Rowland-Seymour, A., & Sharma, R. (2014). Meditation programs for psychological stress and well-being: A systematic review and meta-analysis. *JAMA Internal Medicine, 174*(3), 357–368. https//doi:10.1001/jamainternmed.2013.13018

Greason, P., & Cashwell, C. S. (2009). Mindfulness and counseling self-efficacy: The mediating role of attention and empathy. *Counselor Education and Supervision, 49*, 2–19. https://doi.org/10.1002/j.1556-6978.2009.tb00083.x

Kabat-Zinn, J. (2003). Mindfulness-based interventions in context: Past, present, and future. *Clinical Psychology: Science and Practice, 10*(2), 144–156. https://doi.org/10.1093/clipsy.bpg016

Martin, J. R. (1997). Mindfulness: A proposed common factor. *Journal of Psychotherapy Integration, 7*(4), 291–312. https://doi.org/10.1023/B:JOPI.0000010885.18025.bc

McKay, M., Wood, J. C., & Brantley, J. (2007). *Dialectical Behavior Therapy Skills Workbook: Practical DBT Exercises for Learning Mindfulness, Interpersonal Effectiveness, Emotion Regulation, & Distress Tolerance.* Oakland, CA: New Harbinger Publications.

National Center for Complementary and Integrative Health (n.d.). *Meditation: In Depth.* https://nccih.nih.gov/health/meditation/overview.htm

Nestor, J. (2020). *Breath. The New Science of a Lost Art.* Riverhead Books.

Parker, G. (2020). *Restorative Yoga for Ethnic and Race-Based Stress and Trauma.* Singing Dragon Publications.

Philippot, P., Chapelle, G., & Blairy, S. (2002). Respiratory feedback in the generation of emotion. *Cognition & Emotion, 16*(5), 605–627.

Smith, D. (2014). *Yes, Yoga Has Curves.* Author.

Telles, S., Narendran, S., Raghuraj, P., Nagarathna, R., & Nagendra, H. R. (1997). Comparison of changes in autonomic and respiratory parameters of girls after yoga and games at a community home. *Perceptual and Motor Skills, 84*(1), 251–257.

Villate, V. M. (2015). Yoga for college students: An empowering form of movement and connection. *Physical Educator, 72*(1), 44.

Chapter 5

Mindful Movement

As a reminder, mindfulness is the awareness of *some-thing*, the action of paying attention on purpose in whatever you are doing. How often do you notice yourself paying attention, on purpose, to the way you move your body, the way you sit, the way you walk, the way you breathe, or even the way you think? We often only consider "the way" we do something if there is a problem or if it seems to not be "doing" or "moving" properly. Similarly, when it comes to the body, we tend to only pay attention, on purpose, to its functionality when there is a problem. When an ache or pain comes to our body, we usually begin to receive it as an annoyance. However, what if we paid attention on purpose to the ache or pain as a communication? What if we took the time to mindfully notice the communication and let the mindful movement of our breath, partnered with the body, create space for a full understanding? We can choose to listen to the communicating area of our body and receive the pain or ache as a "love note" that comes as communication to inform us that maybe we need to adjust something in our lives.

Perhaps one of the activities of which we are least mindful is our body movement. Mindful movement is an aspect of yoga called asana. Asana, a Sanskrit word that means "seat" or "posture," is the physical practice and movement of the body that unites the inner and outer person. This type of mindfulness is a partnering with the body to become aware of possible causes of "love notes" or emotional holdings in the body. Movement is like a language that communicates with us and between us without words. Movement shows the inseparability of our mind and our body (Clark et al., 2015). Thus, if we bring mindful awareness to movement, we have found a way to reclaim our bodies. Mindful movements that bring awareness to the breath as well as the inner and outer body are believed to produce change and healing, including feelings of relaxation, happiness, and interconnectedness (Freiler, 2008; Kirkcaldy, 2018; Young, 2008).

As emotions exist throughout our bodies, engaging in mindful movements creates a pathway for us to ground ourselves in body awareness and connect with our emotions. Beyond the obvious mental and physical health benefits associated with physical activity, Salmon (2020) identified additional reasons we should practice mindful movement, such as because it

- Releases a valuable domain of expressions by bringing awareness to the body and its many expressive capabilities;
- Provides a bridge between being sedentary and engaging in physical activity;
- Anchors attention in the present movement while engaging in physical activity (e.g., walking or climbing stairs);
- Encourages a nonjudgmental attitude toward the body because the motions are simple and within most everyone's capabilities and unrealistic demands are not being placed on the body;
- Allows us to become more focused the more mindful movements are practiced.

Sometimes, movement is what the body and mind need. In a study conducted by Penn State (2018), researchers found that when students were more mindful and more active than usual, they reported being less stressed while on their feet and moving. Being more active can reduce negative affect, but by also being more mindful than usual simultaneously, the effect was amplified. With this type of mindfulness of the body, a student can observe and learn to handle their body, their breathing, their feelings, their mental states, and their consciousness. Mindful movement can help a student gain a relationship with their interior world, the world they cannot touch, but still to have a caring, loving, sensual relationship with themselves. Mindful movement can help a student re-activate the self-sensing systems of the body during times of stress. In a heightened body awareness, a student is able to access, detect, and be in touch with the breath, the heartbeat, and body tension. Therefore, mindful movement can serve as a needed and effective facilitator towards healthy, holistic living for students.

As introduced in Chapter 4, emotions, especially undesired emotions, can get locked in certain areas of the body while desired emotions might be blocked from flowing through the body. Mindful movement fosters emotional awareness and release in the body. Asking a student a question such as "where do you feel fear in your body?" can offer accurate identification of the emotion as opposed to avoiding it. Once identified, a mindful movement to move that part of the body can facilitate movement of that emotion. When emotions that are difficult or undesired are avoided, two things can inevitably occur—the hurt plays out and we receive a "love note," or the stress response is activated and the body can stay in a hyper-arousal state. This occurrence is a part of our body's natural somatic language, as the energy of the emotion puts the mind and body together; however, mindful movement (asana) can help move this energy. In turn, the mind becomes focused. In yoga, there are three types of movement (asana) that are considered to move energy, especially emotional energy, in a certain way.

1. Langhana is a Sanskrit word that means "to fast," "reduction," or "to diminish back to its cause." In asana practice, langhana movement and postures are focused on elimination or lightening the body's load. It allows for a clearing and reduction of aggravation. Langhana is related to the exhale and the parasympathetic nervous system, so of course movements will be more relaxing and will slow the heart rate. The postures are described as bringing the fire within back to its balance. There is a relaxation of the breath and metabolism as well as calming of the mind. The postures work to soothe the body and mind.

2. Brahmana is the opposite energetic principle of langhana. It means to grow or expand. These types of movements energize the body and are related to the inhale and to the sympathetic nervous system. These movements are done to move the fire within to the periphery so that one may experience warmth and heat. Energy moves from the center to the periphery. The movements increase mental activity, enhance metabolic functions, and clear undesired emotions. Brahmana movements are especially useful for students desiring healing, awakening, or extra energy. This type of movement might be recommended for depression, lack of confidence, and low energy, as well as to increase self-awareness and joy. This type of movement is also recommended for practice in the morning.

3. Samana is laghana asana, in conjunction with Brahmana asanas, can help bring the body, mind, and spirit into balance. In Sanskrit, this word means "pacification" or "alleviation." The ultimate goal of these movements is to assimilate situations, emotions, challenges, and experiences.

A STUDENT'S VOICE

I have found that mindfulness practice is a very grounding experience. Oftentimes I would come into class with extreme feelings of anxiety and thoughts of what I had to do and complete throughout the day. Starting my Tuesdays and Thursdays with mindfulness helped me ground myself in the present.

—An undergraduate student

MOVING IT ALL TOGETHER

The following movements can be used with a group of students or with an individual student. They can be done alone or in a sequence. After each activity, invite students to discuss what they noticed, sensed, or felt during the practice. Allow the use of these movements to be easy, open, and flexible. Hopefully, with the practice of this very short list of asana poses, students will be open and encouraged to seek out a regular practice on campus or in the local communities.

MOVEMENT (ASANA)

The medicine is in the movement. (LaCretia Dye, 2020)

Cat and Cow (Seated)

Intention: To alleviate sadness and increase self-awareness.

- Have students sit in a chair with their feet hip-width apart and their feet parallel like a perfect number 11 (Mountain Pose). Hands are placed on the ends of knees.

Facilitator says:

- Inhale and begin to take shoulders back, lift chin, gaze towards ceiling, and move belly and chest forward. Arms are up to the sky, palms facing each other.
- Broaden across shoulder blades and draw shoulders away from ears.
- Begin to exhale and move into cat pose, pulling belly towards spine and round back towards back of chair. Don't force chin to chest but easily release head down.
- Inhaling, come back to cow pose, exhale, return to cat pose.
- Continue for three to five breath cycles or six times.
- Relax body (stay here for 5–10 seconds).

(a)   (b)

Chair Twist

Intention: To alleviate anger and increase self-awareness.

- Have students sit in chair with their feet hip-width apart and their feet parallel like a perfect number 11 (Mountain Pose). Hands are placed on lap.

Facilitator says:

- Inhale and begin to take shoulders back, lift chin, gaze towards ceiling, and move belly and chest forward. Arms are up to the sky, palms facing each other.
- Broaden across shoulder blades and draw shoulders away from ears.
- Begin to exhale, into cat pose, pulling belly towards spine and round back towards back of chair. Don't force chin to chest but easily release head down.
- Inhaling, come back to cow pose, exhale, return to cat pose.
- Continue for three to five breath cycles or six times.
- Relax body (stay here for 5–10 seconds).

Energy Flow

Intention: Mindful movement to support body awareness, energy building, and e-motion movement.

    Facilitator says:

- Today, we are going to practice awakening the body and emotions through mindful movement.
- I invite you to stand with your feet hip-width apart, feeling your feet connect to the ground. Hands are at your heart with palms together. Activate your confidence and stand tall like a mountain.

- Begin to notice your breath. Imagine that with each breath in, you inhale energy, and with each breath out, you exhale any feelings of tiredness, confusion, or worry.
- Notice yourself feeling more confident. Take your arms wide with an inhale as you look up and touch fingertips together.
- Begin to exhale, move arms back wide and down, bending the knees and folding at the hips until the fold is complete. Pause.
- Inhale arms wide again, going back to the top as before. Pause when fingertips touch.
- Continue this for five or six more breath cycles. Feel the body warming up, and imagine that with each journey up and down, you are moving the energy around you to wake it up.

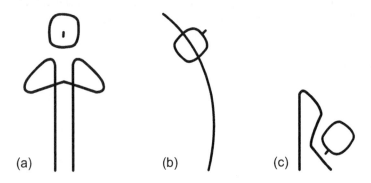

(a) (b) (c)

Focus Flow

Intention: Mindful movement to support body awareness and e-motion movement
   Facilitator says:

- Today, we are going to practice focusing through mindful movement. Let's see how long you can hold your Tree pose today (see description of "Tree Pose" below). How many seconds do you think we should hold our Tree on each side (10–20 seconds suggested)?
- I invite you to stand with your feet hip-width apart, feeling your feet connect to the ground. Activate your strength and stand tall like a mountain with your palms together and hands at your heart.
- Begin to notice your breath. Imagine that with each breath in, you inhale laser focus, and with each breath out, you exhale any feelings of anxiousness, worry, or confusion.

- Notice yourself feeling more calm. Bring all of your weight to your right foot and leg.
- With your left leg, you have two options:
  - Option 1: Lift the left heel and, with the ball of your left foot or toes on the ground, let the left heel rest above the right ankle like a kickstand; or
  - Option 2: Bring your left foot to rest below the knee, on the side of the calf. Your left knee is pointed out to the side.
- Now, standing up nice and tall, find a visual focal point (choose one thing to focus on near you). See if you can stay here for _____ (depending on how many seconds the group decided). Now release and let's repeat this on the other side.
- On your next inhale, bring all of your weight to your left foot and leg.
- With your right leg, you have two options:
  - Option 1: With the ball of your right foot or toes on the ground, let the right heel rest above the right ankle like a kickstand; or
  - Option 2: Bring your right foot to rest below the knee, on the side of the calf. Your right knee is pointed out to the side.
- Now, standing up nice and tall, find that focal point. Now activate your positive self-talk: "I am strong. I am focused. I can do this."
- Let's stay in Tree pose for ____ (depending on how many seconds the group decided).
- Release.
- Now, this time let's grow our Tree.
- On your next inhale, root your right foot into the ground.
- Bring your left foot to toe touch or below the knee. Your left knee is pointed out to the side.
- Now, imagine that you're growing up out of your ankles, your hips, and your shoulders, growing tall.
- Let's raise our hands over our heads, and if you feel like a little extra challenge, sway your branches left and right, staying focused on your focal point.
- Release, taking a deep belly breath in and out.
- On your next inhale, root your left foot into the ground.
- Bring your right foot to toe touch or below the knee. Your right knee is pointed out to the side.
- Now, imagine that you're growing up out of your ankles, your hips, and your shoulders, growing tall.
- Let's raise our hands over our heads, and if you feel like a little extra challenge, sway your branches left and right, staying focused on your focal point.

- Release, taking a deep belly breath in and out.
- While standing, roll your shoulders back, bringing your feet together, and close your eyes.
- Take your left hand and place it on your heart, your right hand on your belly. Begin to notice your breath.
- Imagine that with each breath in, you inhale focus, and with each breath out, you exhale worry.
- Notice how focused you feel—full of confidence, mental strength, emotional strength, and physical strength.

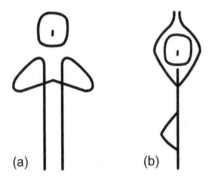

(a)　　　(b)

Forward Fold and Flat-Back

Intention: Mindful movement to support body awareness and e-motion movement.

> *Invite students to stand up next to their chair/desk. Facilitator says*:

- While standing, with palms together and hands at your heart, begin to notice your breath.
- Take an inhale, take your arms wide with an inhale as you look up and touch fingertips together.
- Pause, and on the exhale, fold forward with a slight bend in the knees. Allow a gentle ease and lengthen to the muscles on the back of the legs (hamstrings).
- On the next inhale, take hands to shins, creating a flat back and lengthening the spine.
- Exhale again and fold again with lengthening to the back of the legs.
- Inhale once more to a flat back.
- Notice which position feels better; hang out there for three more breaths.

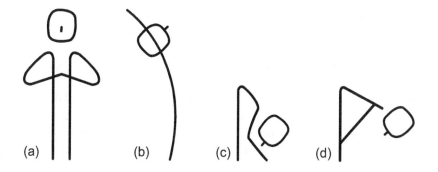

(a) (b) (c) (d)

Strength Flow

Intention: Mindful movement to support body awareness and e-motion movement. *Invite students to stand up behind their chair/desk. Facilitator says*:

- While standing behind your chair, with palms together and hands at your heart, begin to notice your breath; imagine that with each breath in, you inhale strength, and with each breath out, you exhale weakness (or fear, anger, and frustration).
- On the next inhale, lift the right knee with exceptional awareness high, just like you are preparing to march; exhale and bring your foot down to the ground.
- On the next inhale, lift the left knee high and exhale, releasing your left foot down to the ground.
- Now, for the next ten steps, we will move in this manner like you are marching.
  - Students can go in any direction; the goal is to release undesired emotions such as fear, anger, and frustration.
- By doing this walk, we will use that energy to build our strength.
  - Invite students to march back to their space to begin the mindful movement sequence, letting the energy of strength flow through their entire body.
- Stand behind your chair with your feet at the perfect number 11, one foot next to the other and hip-width apart, with arms along your sides. Inhale and begin to take your arms wide up to the sky, bringing the fingers toward each other.
- Look up at your fingers and touch your fingertips together. Exhale and bend your knees, take the arms down and wide as you begin to fold over your legs like you are a waterfall.

- Pause here, and as you hang, imagine that your upper body is a waterfall coming from your legs. On your next inhale, take your arms wide and go all the way back up, look up at your hands, and touch your fingertips.
- Bend your knees, exhale, and bring your arms back down, coming into Waterfall.
- With your knees bent, one more time, inhale and bring yourself all the way up. Touch your fingertips. Exhale as you bring palms together and bring hands down to the front of your heart. Now release your hands to hang at your sides.
- Take your hands to the back of your chair, step your left foot back, release your heel down to the earth, and then inhale coming up into Warrior 1 (description for Warrior 1 Pose is below). Exhale to Warrior 2 (description for Warrior 2 Pose is below).
- Now in one easy swoop, step forward and come back to Mountain.
- Let's do the same on the other side.
- Inhale all the way up, look up, bringing your hands together, pause, exhale, bend your knees, and go all the way down into Waterfall. Inhale up again, looking up at your hands, pause, bend your knees, and exhale all the way down into Waterfall. One more time, inhale all the way up, Upward Mountain, exhale and go to Waterfall.
- Take your hands to the back of your chair, step your right foot back, bring your heel down and then inhale and come up to Warrior 1. Exhale to Warrior 2. Stay here and breathe in and out.
- On your next inhale in one easy swoop, step forward into Mountain.
- While standing, roll your shoulders back, bring your feet together, and close your eyes.
- Take your left hand and place it on your heart, and place your right hand on your belly. Begin to notice your breath.
- Imagine that with each breath in, you inhale strength, and with each breath out, you exhale weakness (or fear, anger, and frustration).
- On the next inhale, lift the right knee high, just like you are an elephant preparing to march; exhale and stomp your right foot to the ground.
- On the next inhale, lift the left knee high, exhale, and stomp your left foot down to the ground.
- Now, notice the strength flowing through your entire body.
- For the next ten steps, we will move in the elephant march again.
- This time notice how much stronger you feel—more grounded and connected to the earth, full of confidence, mental strength, emotional strength, and physical strength.

(a)   (b)   (c)   (d)

Tree Pose

Intention: To alleviate anxious feelings and create intentional focus.

- Have students stand with their feet hip-width apart and their feet parallel like a perfect number 11 (Mountain Pose).

Facilitator says:

- Inhale and bring all of your weight to the right foot.
- There are three options with your left leg:
  - Option 1: Come on the ball of the left foot, with the left heel resting above the right ankle like a kickstand;
  - Option 2: Bring the bottom of the left foot to rest below the knee on the side of the right calf; or
  - Option 3: Put the bottom of the left foot to the inside of right thigh (never on the knee). Left knee is pointed out to the left side.
- Stand up tall and find a focal point (one thing to focus on). Bring palms together and move them to the heart to help with balance. Stay in this position for 5 seconds.
- Release and repeat on other side.
  - *Note*:
    - If students feel balanced and focused, have them grow their tree tall and raise their branches (arms) toward the sky. Stay here for 5 seconds.
    - If students fall, have them get back up—similar to how we fall in life, and then get back up.
- Release foot to the floor.

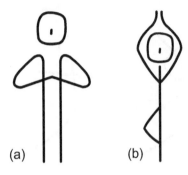

(a)   (b)

Waterfall

Intention: To practice mindful movement and release tension in upper body.

- Have students stand with their feet hip-width apart and their feet parallel like a perfect number 11 (Mountain Pose).

Facilitator says:

- Inhale and begin to take arms up to the sky, palms facing each other.
- Look up and bring hands to touch.
- Begin to exhale, taking arms wide and down. Begin to bend knees and forward fold over. Once folded forward, arms and head hang loosely as fingers dangle right above the floor or below the knee. Bend elbows as you take hands and grab opposite elbows.
- Relax neck and begin to sway upper body right to left (move this way for 5–10 seconds).

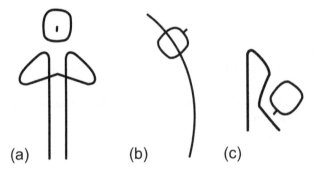

(a)   (b)   (c)

Warrior 1

Intention: Practice mindful movement and bring inner strength awareness.
   Note: This activity can be practiced with or without a chair.

- Have students stand with their feet hip-width apart and their feet parallel like a perfect number 11 (Mountain Pose).

Facilitator says:

- Put hands on the back of your chair, bending the right knee, step left foot back about 3–4 feet and release left heel down to the earth at a 45-degree angle.
- Balance your weight between left foot and right foot while hips are squared and facing forward. Now exhale as you bend the right knee a bit deeper over the right ankle.
- Reach up strongly to the sky through your arms. Keep palms and fingers active and reaching.
- Hold for up to 15 seconds and release.
- Now lower arms to the back of the chair and repeat with right leg.

(a)   (b)

Warrior 2

Intention: Practice mindful movement and bring inner strength awareness.

- Have students stand with their feet hip-width apart and their feet parallel like a perfect number 11 (Mountain Pose).

Facilitator says:

- Exhale as you step your left foot back about 4–5 ft, bending the right knee.
- The right toes are pointed forward. The left foot is pointed at 90 degrees. Left toes should be pointed to the left side of the room or space.
- Raise both arms to shoulder height, parallel to the floor. The arms are aligned directly over the legs (right wrist in front of right knee and left wrist over left ankle).
- With palms facing down, reach actively from fingertip to fingertip.
- Turn head to gaze out across the tip of the right middle finger.
- Hold for 15 seconds.
- To release, inhale as you press down through the back foot and straighten the front leg. Lower arms.
- Repeat other side by beginning in Warrior 1 pose (left knee forward).

(a)   (b)

TAKE A MOMENT

Take a brief moment and ask yourself or others the following questions.

- How might my own assumptions and level of confidence influence my ability to engage in mindful movements?
- What thoughts might keep me from engaging in mindful movements?
- How comfortable am I in checking in with my body? Will I listen to what it is telling me that I need?
- What are my thoughts about incorporating mindful movements into my everyday life?

NOW MORE THAN EVER, STUDENTS NEED TO MOVE

Did you know that unless we are asleep, we as humans are designed to move? As you might recall from Chapter 2, our reptilian brain (central nervous system) controls our instinctual actions to sense change around us and move us through environments to keep us alive. For nearly 200,000 years, we *homo sapiens* spent our time on the move, and we moved for survival. To eat and shelter ourselves, we moved, hunted, and dug from the ground. Our bodies are built to move, and in turn, movement keeps us healthy. However, within just the last century, our health and survival have been compromised because of a simple four-legged object—the chair. Within this last century, we have allowed the chair and the convenience of technology to bring our bodies to be almost completely sedentary, and not just in the way we work and play, but also in the way we shop and travel. Americans, on average, spend more than 8 hours sitting per day (Levine, 2014; 2015; Ussery et al., 2018).

Sitting too much has been shown to create poor blood circulation, damage nerves, and increase heart attack risk, cholesterol levels, and blood sugar levels (Levine, 2014). Our sedentary lives—behaviors involving decreased energy expenditures during our waking hours that include sitting, reclining, and lying down (Pate et al., 2008)—are causing our hip flexors and abdominals to shrink as well as lower back and neck pain and diaphragm dysfunction. When we sit too much, our body is forced into uncomfortable positions, which ultimately leads to compromised function, both internally and externally. This societal practice and sedentary lifestyle are damaging not just to our bodies but also to our minds and spirit. Now more than ever, students need to move.

The number of hours students sit in class, at desks, in front of computers and electronic devices, eating, driving in their cars, and socializing with friends only increases their sedentary lifestyle. Recognizing the risks of a sedentary life, higher education professionals can help students explore facilitators and barriers to engaging in a less sedentary lifestyle as well as with developing functional interventions to decrease this behavior to hopefully avert a long-term sedentary lifestyle and habit of not moving. Using the suggestions and activities in this chapter can help with getting students to begin with small movements that will also help enhance their awareness and build their body and mind.

Below is a case study about a college student who is facing some life challenges and experiencing stress and anxiety. Read the case and reflect on the questions that follow or engage in a discussion with a group.

THE CASE

Lexi is a 17-year-old Caucasian female in her sophomore year of college at your institution. Academically, Lexi has been a strong student and is often praised and recommended for academic awards by her professors. In confidence, Lexi shares with you that she has a difficult time changing channels in her mind when challenges occur in her life and that she has an especially hard time discussing her feelings of hurt, confusion, or rage. Specifically, Lexi described challenges relative to her close friends and family, indicating that she felt confused about her relationships with them, specifically her mom. She states that she often feels hurt by her mother but cannot not identify any specific words or behaviors that caused this hurt. Lexi shows you her left arm and right leg and states, "When I don't know why I feel hurt by them, I do this," revealing deep scratches on her arm and leg. Lexi then explains that it takes time for her to open up and trust others, and it was difficult for her to share her feelings and behavior with you. She then admits that she "was in counseling" some years ago but did not think that she has needed a counselor since she began college. However, she admits that she has often been anxious and stressed since her freshman year and spends most of her time during the weekdays in class, studying, completing assignments, and sitting at a desk of her work-study job on campus. On the weekends, she tries to keep up with her class assignments, but breaks to watch some shows and movies on Netflix and Hulu and peruse social media. She reports that a few times, she has gone to the movies or out to eat with friends. During "down moments," she admits that her mind tends to wander, she becomes a bit overwhelmed with her emotions, and she thinks about how she would like her life to be different and "better," but is not sure how to make a change. She says that when she has these thoughts, she becomes more sad, stressed, and anxious.

Reflection and Discussion Questions

- What are the key facts in this case?
- What concerns do you have about Lexi's well-being?
- Summarize the tensions and challenges to Lexi's well-being.
- Based on what you have read in the first five chapters, what are some actions and strategies you would recommend to Lexi to help her address the challenges and tensions?
- Based on what you have read in the first five chapters, what are some actions and strategies you would recommend to Lexi to help her work on decreasing her stress and anxiety?

REFERENCES

Clark, D., Schumann, F., & Mostofsky, S. H. (2015). Mindful movement and skilled attention. *Frontiers in Human Neuroscience*, *9*, 297. https://doi.org/10.3389/fnhum.2015.00297

Dye, R. (2020). Poses [Original Drawing].

Freiler, T. (2008). Learning through the body. *New Directions for Adult and Continuing Education*, *119*, 37–47. https://doi.org/10.1002/ace.304

Kirkcaldy, B. (2018). *Psychotherapy, Literature and the Visual and Performing Arts*. Palgrave Macmillan. https://doi.org/10.1007/978-3-319-75423-9

Levine, J. A. (2014). *Get Up!: Why Your Chair is Killing You and What You Can Do About It*. Macmillan.

Levine, J. A. (2015). Sick of sitting. *Diabetologia*, *58*(8), 1751–1758. https://doi.org/10.1007/s00125-015-3624-6

Pate, R. R., O'Neill, J. R., & Lobelo, F. (2008). The evolving definition of sedentary. *Exercise and Sport Sciences Reviews*, *36*,173–178. https://doi.org/10.1097/jes.0b013e3181877d1a

Penn State (2018, June 21). Mindful movement may help lower stress, anxiety. *Science News*. https://www.sciencedaily.com/releases/2018/06/180621112007.htm

Salmon, P. (2020). *Mindful Movement in Psychotherapy*. The Guilford Press.

Ussery, E. N., Fulton, J. E., Galuska, D. A., Katzmarzyk, P. T., & Carlson, S. A. (2018). Joint Prevalence of Sitting Time and Leisure-Time Physical Activity among US Adults, 2015–2016. *JAMA*, *320*(19), 2036–2038. https://doi.org/10.1001/jama.2018.17797

Young, C. (2008). The history and development of body-psychotherapy: The American legacy of Reich. *Body, Movement and Dance in Psychotherapy*, *3*(1), 5–18. https://doi.org/10.1080/17432970701717783

Helping Students with Focus and Choices for Change

Let's imagine you are a college instructor and Hannah is a student in one of your classes. Hannah has consistently submitted unfinished work or late work since the class began and in another class you taught the previous semester. After the mid-point of the semester, Hannah asks to meet with you to discuss her concerns about her performance in the course. Let's say that at that meeting, you discuss how her lack of completion and performance on assignments are impacting her grade negatively; refer her to the rubrics for each assignment; ask her if there are any barriers that are hindering her from completing the assignments; refer her to the writing lab; and offer to answer any questions for any future assignments. Hannah then tells you that she is on academic probation and if she does not earn a grade of at least a "C" in the course, she will have to leave the university for a semester, which she reports is causing an immense amount of stress for her. She follows that statement by also telling you how she is having a family issue, her daily schedule keeps her busy, her roommate is loud, she does not fully understand the assignments, she works part time, and sometimes she has problems staying motivated because college is hard and she is ready to graduate. She then asks you if she can complete an extra credit assignment or is there something you can do to help her earn a grade of "C" since she really wants to finish college, especially since she is so close to the end. Let's say that you ask Hannah what she finds difficult in completing the assignments so that you can gauge where the issue lies. Hannah simply responds that she tries her best, she's never really been a good writer because her prior professors did not push her enough, she has not received feedback about how to improve her writing in former classes, she is not sure what you are looking for in the assignment (although there are rubrics), and there are only so many hours in the day to meet all the demands in her life. Let's say that before ending the meeting, you review the upcoming assignments as well as the rubrics with Hannah and answer her questions. For the next due assignment, Hannah's assignment is again partially completed, earning a failing grade, and she is requesting another meeting with you.

What do you think about this scenario? How would you respond to Hannah's request for another meeting? If you met with her, what would you say? How do you balance helping a student through stressful and anxious moments and your expectation that they take responsibility for their choices and actions? What strategies can you use to help facilitate a change?

A STUDENT'S VOICE

It is hard for me to relax when college can be so stressful, but I look forward to these activities each time to feel the impact of breathing, being still, and focusing on my growth even for a few minutes. I now continue to do this on my own because I have seen such a change in myself and my lifestyle due to it.

—An undergraduate student

Of course, college can be challenging and overwhelming, but college students are also emerging adults who make choices, with consequences, and behave accordingly. College students are presented with numerous opportunities to make choices about their life, such as choosing a major, joining an organization, drinking, smoking, completing an internship, and beginning a job search. Once in college, students are asked to take a higher level of responsibility for their education and their decisions. Although taking on this role can present challenges for students, the process of making decisions during college can help prepare students for navigating the complexities of adulthood. As a higher education professional, you may decide that you will attempt to help them with decision-making, while understanding that you are not making decisions for them. This process can be especially poignant when students are stressed and anxious and looking to you for wise words and direction. During these moments, we should acknowledge that traditional college students grow along a certain developmental trajectory. Nevitt Sanford, a psychologist who studied the interaction between social systems and personality, hypothesized about the role of challenge, support, and readiness for students when they meet challenges, such as those associated with focus, change, and decision-making. According to Sanford (1962), many learning experiences for college students require a balance of challenge (intrinsic and extrinsic) and support as they progress through significant personal growth and development, much of which is influenced by the college environment—inside and outside of the classroom. Particularly, individuals grow when faced with a challenge they have the capacity to approach and overcome, psychologically and physically.

109

With too much support, the student may not learn to grow and think differently, and with too much challenge, the student can become frustrated and can possibly quit trying or may regress or rebel, yielding no growth. Sanford (1966) further alluded to levels of developmental readiness, noting that the student must be ready for the challenge to be successful in developing through the challenge, which includes their maturity, acknowledging that they cannot grow until they are physically or psychologically ready to grow. Therefore, as higher education professionals engage in helping students with focus and choices, there must be a balance of support and challenge when the student is ready to take action toward change.

Higher education professionals can help students by providing them with information and strategies that could enhance their focus, decision-making process, ability to make a change, and management of their negative emotions while facilitating their understanding of taking personal responsibility. Within the context of choice theory, there is focus on the present with emphasis on a person learning to develop a strong internal locus of control (i.e., belief that one can attain desired results through one's choices) and a strong sense of responsibility for one's behavior (Glasser, 1998). Choice theory teaches that we choose all that we do, and we are responsible for what we choose, meaning that we choose both our misery and our happiness. The theoretical framework of choice theory, a counseling paradigm, and the WDEP procedures will serve as the framework for discussing how higher education professionals can help students understand how they make decisions that can add to or subtract from their well-being.

CHOICE THEORY

Choice theory, developed by William Glasser (1998), explains why and how people function. An internal control psychology, choice theory explains how and why we make the choices that determine the course of our lives. This theoretical approach is the basis for reality therapy, which provides the delivery system for helping individuals take more effective control of their lives. Choice theory posits that we are not born blank slates waiting to be motivated by forces in the world around us. Rather, we are born with and motivated by five genetically encoded basic needs that drive us all our lives (Glasser, 1998). These needs are survival, love and belonging, power or achievement, freedom or independence, and fun.

1. Survival includes physiological essentials that sustain our lives, including good health, nourishment, shelter, quality air, safety, security, and physical comfort.

2. Love and belonging include our loving another or others and being loved; being connected to others, such as friends, family, intimate partners, colleagues, and groups with whom we affiliate; and being in contact and having interactions with those to whom we feel connected.

3. Power or achievement involves our desire to matter; feelings of accomplishment and competence; self-esteem, success, and control over one's own life; and recognition, respect, making a difference, and leaving a legacy.

4. Freedom and independence are about having choices and our ability to make choices; to move freely without restriction; to love without undue and unnecessary limits or constraints; to be independent and autonomous; and to be creative.

5. Fun and enjoyment include our pleasure; our ability to laugh, joke, and play; our opportunity to relax and have relevant learning; and our appreciation of being human.

Each person has all five needs; however, they vary in strength. Of course, sometimes what we think are needs are actually "wants," which needs to be clarified as we are navigating the world making responsible decisions that bring us closer to meeting unmet needs and goals. Choice theory explains that everything we do is chosen and every behavior is our best attempt to get what we want to satisfy one or more of our basic needs (Glasser, 2001). Emotional, mental, and behavioral problems can arise when one of our needs is not met.

This theoretical approach emphasizes that shortly after birth and continuing all through life, individuals store information inside their minds and build a file of wants called the *Quality World*. This world is the one we would like to live in if we could. It is completely based on our wants and personal needs and these are very specific. This somewhat imaginary world consists of specific images of people, activities, events, beliefs, situations, and possessions that fulfill our needs (Wubbolding, 2000). In addition, people are the most important components of the Quality World, and what we care about and want most is to have a relationship with others.

Choice theory requires the artful integration of rapport and helping skills (i.e., attending behaviors, listening skills, nonjudgment, facilitative self-disclosure, and summarizing) in a helping relationship (Wubbolding, 2000). Before discussing any issues and strategies, a trusting and supportive relationship between the professional and the student is paramount. This type of relationship is especially needed because some students may have faced situations where trust was minimal (e.g., authoritative parents, unexpected disappointments in life due to others, unfaithful relationships, gang situations). You providing a safe space, while possessing and presenting warmth, sincerity, acceptance, concern, understanding, openness, and respect for the student are cornerstones to developing a successful relationship to help others to genuinely be open to the idea of evaluating their decision-making and what is helpful or harmful to their well-being.

Choice theory teaches that total behavior is made up of four distinct components—acting, thinking, feeling, and physiology—that accompany all our thoughts, feelings, and actions. This theoretical approach emphasizes thinking and acting. The primary emphasis is on what the individual is doing and how the doing component influences the other components of total behavior. Behavior is purposeful because it is designed to close the gap between what we want and what we perceive we are getting. The brain is the control system that helps with this alignment. By assessing the impact and success of our behaviors, we can determine whether we need to make a change and, if so, what resourceful strategies we can use to modify our thoughts, emotions, and behaviors. In essence, since our behaviors come from within, we therefore choose our destiny.

An underlying assumption of choice theory is that we cannot change other people, but can only control ourselves and our choices. Realistically, other factors such as upbringing, culture, environment, demographic dimensions, and genetics can impact our decisions; however, in the end, our choices ultimately impact our outcomes. To discover what we want and identify our choices to obtain or achieve what we want or how to fulfill our needs, and evaluate how our actions contribute to or detract from our goals, we need the tools to plan the achievement of our goals. The WDEP is a set of procedures that can be used to move through this process.

APPLYING WDEP TO HELP COLLEGE STUDENTS

The acronym WDEP was developed by Wubbolding (2000), and each letter represents a cluster of appropriate skills and techniques for assisting others to take better control of their lives and thereby fulfill their needs in ways that are satisfying to them and to society. Wubbolding expressed these elements in a way that makes them easy to remember: W=wants, needs, and perceptions; D=direction and doing; E=self-evaluation; and P=planning. The goal is to weave these components together in ways that can lead an individual to evaluate their lives and to decide to move in more effective directions. The goal or desired outcome is a change in behavior resulting in need satisfaction and greater happiness. For example, when working with a college student who is experiencing anxiety because of academic problems, you would attempt first to develop a positive relationship with the student. When this has been achieved, by means of active listening and skillful questioning, you could move on to the WDEP procedures and use them as a guide. Your aim is to discover their wants, needs, and perceptions.

Wants, Needs, and Perceptions (W)

As all wants are related to the five basic needs, the key question is, "What do you want?" The students would be asked to describe what they want ("W") for themselves and the world around them. You could also ask about their level of commitment (Wubbolding, 1988, 1996), such as "How hard are you willing to work at solving the problem or gaining a better sense of control for yourself?" Some useful questions to help students pinpoint what they want include:

1. If you were the person you wish you were, what kind of person would you be?
2. If your wants and your family's wants matched, what would your family be like?
3. What would you be doing if you were living as you want to live?
4. Do you really want to change your life?
5. What do you think stops you from making the changes you want to make?

Wubbolding and Brickell (2009) included questions focused on perceptions:

1. What is your perspective of the situation?
2. What do you think you can control?

These are important questions for discussion as most people have more control in their lives than they often perceive, and these questions are designed to help them move from a sense of external control to a sense of internal control.

This line of questioning sets the stage for moving through the other procedures in this theoretical approach. It is an art to know which questions to ask, how to ask them, and when to ask them. Relevant questions can help students gain insight and prepare them for developing plans for change. It is important to note that although well-timed, open-ended questions can help students identify their goals, excessive questioning can result in resistance and defensiveness.

Directions and Doing (D)

The next step in the procedures is the "D," which involves questions about what the student is doing and where the student's current behavior is taking them. Even though problems may be rooted in the past, students are encouraged to

113

learn to deal with them in the present by learning better ways to get what they want. Problems must be solved either in the present or in the future. It is essential to discuss with students the overall direction of their lives, including where they are going and where their behavior is taking them. You could ask if their current behavior is leading them in the direction where they want to be in a month, a year, or two years. The focus at this time should be on helping the student increase their awareness of what their choices look like from a distance. The focus is on gaining awareness of and changing current behavior. To accomplish this, focus on questions like these:

1. "What are you doing now?"
2. "What did you do yesterday"
3. "What did you want to do differently last week?"
4. "What actually stopped you from doing what you wanted to do?"
5. "What do you plan to do tomorrow?"

Self-Evaluation (E)

At this point ("E"), students are asked to conduct a self-evaluation. Glasser (1972) described evaluation as the basis for change, the cornerstone of the WDEP system, and as the keystone in the arch of procedures. You can ask the student to describe their behavior, their wants, their perceptions, and their levels of commitment and then to make judgments about them. Ask the student to consider whether their present behavior is helping them or hurting them, important or unimportant, meaningful or meaningless, and to their advantage or not to their advantage. At that specific time when people begin to change is when they evaluate what they are doing and then begin to answer the question, "Is it helping?" Usually, people do not change until they decide that what they are doing is not helping them to accomplish what they want.

Artful questioning assists students in evaluating their present behavior and the direction it is taking them. Wubbolding (2000, 2011, 2015) suggests the following questions:

1. Is what you are doing helping or hurting you?
2. Is what you are doing now what you want to be doing?
3. Is your behavior working for you or against you?
4. Is what you want realistic or attainable?
5. Is it true that you have no control over your situation?
6. How committed are you to changing your life?
7. After carefully examining what you want, does it appear to be in your best interest?

8. After carefully examining what you want, does it appear to be in the best interest of others?

Such questions can help the student evaluate the quality of their actions and make choices that are better for their well-being. Without an honest self-assessment, it is unlikely that students will change.

Planning (P)

The last step in the system of procedures is the "P," which refers to the action plan. The expected outcome is the formulation and follow-through of an effective action plan. The goal is for the student to formulate a plan of action that fulfills their wants and needs without infringing on the rights of others. Effective plans are simple, attainable, measurable, immediate, involving, consistent, committed to, and controlled (SAMI2C3) by the student. The most effective plans originate with the student.

Wubbolding (2000) suggests that an individual can gain more effective control over their lives with plans that have the following characteristics:

- The plan is within the limits of the motivation and capacities of the individual. You may ask them, "What plans could you agree to now that would result in a more satisfying life?"
- Good plans are simple and easy to understand, realistically doable, flexible, and open to revision as the individual gains a deeper understanding of the specific behaviors they want to change.
- The plan involves a positive course of action, and it is stated in terms of what the individual is willing to do.
- The individual is encouraged to develop plans that they can carry out independent of what others do.
- Effective plans are repetitive and, ideally, performed daily.
- Plans are carried out as soon as possible.
- Plans involve process-centered activities. For example, a student may plan to do any of the following: apply for a job, take a yoga class, enhance their overall GPA, devote two hours a week to volunteer work, substitute nutritious food for junk food, join an exercise class, or take a vacation that they have been wanting to take.
- Before carrying out their plans, it is a good idea for the student to evaluate them with a qualified individual, such as a higher education professional, to determine whether they are realistic and attainable.
- After plans have been carried out in real life, it is useful to evaluate them again and make any revisions that may be necessary.

- To help students commit themselves to their plans, it is useful for them to put their plans in writing.

Plans are empty unless there is a commitment to carry them out. It is up to the student to determine how to take their plans outside the restricted world and into the everyday world.

Change can happen if a student can evaluate their own unique and systemic behaviors and follow up with the formulation and implementation of specific plans. If the initial plan does not work for any reason, you can collaborate with the student to devise a different plan. The plan is important as it gives the student a starting point. These procedures (WDEP) could be used with a college student who is concerned with academic problems, homesick, experiencing financial difficulty, has looked unsuccessfully for a job, and/or is having trouble making friends.

When helping a student get through stressful and anxious moments, it is important to allow them to tell their story as they see it. This will help you to determine the perceived locus of control of the student, that is, how much responsibility the student has taken for past behavior. This will also indicate how much responsibility the student can realistically be expected to assume for immediate future choices (Wubbolding, 2000). Accepting full responsibility for and assuming control over our behavior and choices can be seen as a huge undertaking.

What is important is that we do not create an enabling environment that will not allow the student to examine what they are doing, thinking, and feeling or engage in personal growth and self-evaluation. Considering that a student's decision-making could alleviate stressful and anxious moments in their lives, helping them to focus and develop awareness could be beneficial. To help students focus on what they can do that is within their control and to foster a self-evaluation of their choices, you can encourage them to:

- Focus on the present and not the past, which allows them to tune in and refocus their attention.
- Focus their energy on changing their thoughts and behavior.
- Assess if their thoughts are productive to their decision-making and how those thoughts are dictating their choices and actions.
- Let their inner voice be kind to them by trying to avoid negative self-talk, self-blame, self-criticism, and comparing themselves to others.
- Understand that making changes to their thoughts, choices, and behaviors can be difficult; so, give themselves some leniency.
- Recognize that behavior paired with an excuse, regardless if it is real or not, shifts the responsibility from them and the source.
- Make specific plans with attainable goals that take into account their resources.

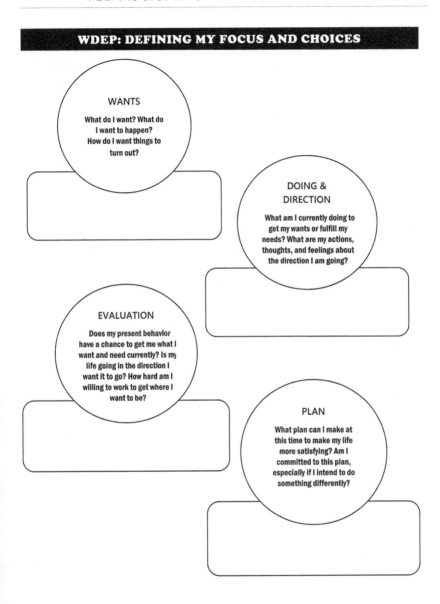

USING WDEP FOR GROUPS WITH A CIRCLE

The use of circles with groups offers a safe, welcoming, and receptive space that moves from person to person, where everyone can see each other and talk honestly, and where all voices can be heard. As such, the circle creates a place that invites sharing and story and facilitates group cohesion. Circles also offer an opportunity for all involved to collectively learn and find solutions and build their confidence and skills. With a focus on each individual in the group, the use of circles with groups tend to be progressive, change-oriented, and innately democratic. A common factor in the success of circles with groups is the value of relationships through building collaboration and respect within the group.

The *Circle-Up* is a powerful communal learning tool that gives students practice in speaking and listening while fulfilling the need for belonging and connection (Glasser, 2008). Perhaps the real power of Circle-Ups is that the students first have an opportunity to connect with one another and talk freely about their problem with attention focused on them when it is their turn.

If deemed more appropriate, higher education professionals can also introduce students to the idea of Circle-Ups by involving a group of students in planned discussions focusing on decision-making and problem solving. These discussions can be used to help solve personal, class, or academic problems. The goal is to teach students to use choice theory in their lives and academics. The group could meet one time or multiple times, depending on the group size and the amount of discussion that needs to occur.

An emphasis should be made to students about how the system works by explaining that the only person you can control is yourself, so each person in the Circle-Up is responsible for deciding what they will do to solve their problem regardless of what others think. Be sure to tell them that everyone will respect everyone, and only one person will speak at a time. Besides, learning this form of interpersonal communication can become a useful life-long skill for the students. Notably, in facilitating the Circle-Up, higher education professionals must possess the personal choice theory qualities of warmth, sincerity, congruence, understanding, acceptance, concern, openness, and respect for the individual (Corey, 2017).

To begin the first Circle-Up, ask students to arrange their chairs in a circle. You can say, "Notice, I could have arranged the chairs in the circle before you arrived and designated specific seats for each but I thought it would be better for us to do this together. This is our group and the more you bring things up for discussion, the more we will be able to help one another." Next, tell them some things about yourself, what you do, and why. Then, ask members of the group to introduce themselves.

Now, introduce the WDEP system to the students—as a pedagogical tool useful for understanding and teaching the concepts.Let them know that it is easy to follow. Explain that each letter represents a cluster of possible skills and techniques for assisting individuals to take better control of their lives and thereby fulfill their needs in ways that are satisfying to them and to society.

Wants, Needs, and Perceptions (W)

Ask for a volunteer to start the discussion by talking about what they want or need help with at this time. Ask each to identify their "wants" and "needs." Continue the discussion until each student has had the opportunity to participate. Allow students to discuss what they have heard and tell them that the group will discuss the area of "doing and direction" next. Be sensitive to students who are reluctant to talk and gently encourage them to get involved, but do not pressure students. Some may sit quietly, participating little, yet get a lot out of the process. For most of them, the idea that they have learned something that is relevant and useful outside of class could be a very positive revelation.

Direction and Doing (D)

Next as a group, discuss what we are "doing" and the "direction" this is leading us in. Present ideas for consideration to the students when necessary. The focus at this point must be on helping the students to increase their awareness of the possible consequences of their choices. It is essential to discuss with students the overall direction of their lives, including where they are going and where their behavior is leading them.

Self-Evaluation (E)

After exploring wants, needs, and perceptions and discussing direction and doing, "self-evaluation" is the next step, which is the cornerstone of the WDEP system and the basis of change. Ask the students to describe their behavior, wants, perceptions, and levels of commitment and then to make judgments about these. Through questioning from the facilitator (i.e., the higher education professional) and comments from peers in the group, students are helped to determine if what they are doing is helping them and leading them in the direction they want their lives to go as they work toward reaching their goals. After a rigorous discussion, students can be more prepared to explore other possible behaviors and formulate plans for action.

Planning (P)

At this point, the focus is on helping students formulate structured plans for change. The process of developing and carrying out plans enables students to begin to gain effective control of their lives. The plan gives students a starting point. The most effective plans originate within students and should be stated in terms of what the students are willing to do. They should be flexible and open to revision as students gain a deeper understanding of the specific behaviors they want to change.

Encourage the students to put their plans in writing. If needed, Circle-Ups can be scheduled periodically through the semester to see how students are doing. Be sure to always listen when students want to talk and support students as they attempt to make more effective and responsible choices related to their wants and needs.

TAKE A MOMENT

Before you begin helping a student evaluate how to make choices that will enhance their well-being, take a moment and ask yourself the following questions.

- What do you believe are the primary motivators for an individual to make a change?
- What would frustrate you in terms of a student's progress toward a set goal or resolution of an issue/concern?
- What factors do you believe influence an individual's behavior, motivation, and decision methods?
- What issues are you uncomfortable discussing with students?
- What emotions that a student expresses would make you uncomfortable?
- What do you consider as necessary coping skills for an individual to possess for them to contribute to their optimal development and wellness over their life span?

In congruence with choice theory, if we are more aware of what we are doing and its consequences for our health, the more conscious choices we can make to develop a plan for our health, such as the practice of mindfulness and self-care. Within choice theory and mindfulness, there is a focus on our actions, thoughts, and feelings as well as our physical, psychological, emotional, social, and spiritual dimensions. Therefore, in tandem with each other, in using the components of choice theory and mindfulness strategies, we can find ways to improve, heal, and grow toward well-being.

CHOICE THEORY AND MINDFULNESS

In accordance with choice theory (Glasser, 1998), we make more conscious choices about our well-being and the practice of self-care when we are more aware of what we are doing and the consequences for our health. A journey toward better health includes a series of choices and awareness, which are also both important on a path to mindfulness and in choice theory. According to Glasser (1992), the processes that lead to change are based on two specific assumptions—a person's present behavior is not getting them what they want, and humans are motivated to change when they believe they can choose other behaviors that will get them closer to what they want. When we want to improve our well-being because we are unsatisfied and unsettled, we will be motivated to change to get what we want and make choices accordingly. Aligning choice theory and mindfulness strategies can provide a framework for the process of our personal growth and well-being, combining the elements of awareness, attention, choice, intention, and attitude to form movement toward our goal. Both focus on the encouragement of greater awareness of thoughts and feelings as well as self-reflection of our reality—examination of our thoughts that trigger our emotions and moods, and how we can modify our thoughts, moods, and patterns through the use of attained skills. As such, when working with students who are stressed, anxious, or distressed, using principles from both choice theory and mindfulness can lead to beneficial strategies to help move the student toward better mental health. Consider the following:

- You can encourage the student to use self-reflection exercises to acquire knowledge and understanding of any barriers that may keep them from moving forward, such as the negative feedback loop and negative self-talk. They can identify distressing thoughts and actions, which will help them take control of their thoughts and emotions.
- You can encourage the student to evaluate their behavior and choices that conflict with their life goals, such as earning their college degree or starting a career in a specific field. They can be aware and bring their attention to their present with this self-evaluation. When we consider a situation in a mindful state, our awareness can allow us to have a better chance to see the choices available and to make judicious choices.
- You can encourage the student to make a diagnostic examination of people, factors, ideas, and beliefs that reflect what they want, and compare those to what they have. If there is a gap between the two, encourage them to apply engaging and evaluating processes to reflect on their needs, their wants, the Quality World pictures they have created, and what they can do to move toward for self-fulfillment.

121

- You can encourage students to create positive relationships that are healthy and supportive, especially since social support and belonging are considered basic human needs. Encourage the student to re-evaluate any relationship that is draining their energy and realize that it is their choice to make a change to those dynamics. Difficult relationships with self and others are the source of most lasting sadness, which can cause us to go into fight/flight/freeze mode and influence us to disconnect from others, which creates additional stress, social alienation, and isolation.

- You can encourage the student to find a way to foster greater self-acceptance and restructure their life by taking responsibility and applying non-controlling and non-blaming techniques to make changes for their well-being. This approach is especially relevant when plans are not working out as intended.

- You can use the procedures of WDEP and SAMI2C3 to encourage the student to move forward to change by evaluating their wants and direction as well as formulating a realistic and attainable plan that represents the elements that increase its success—simple, attainable, measurable, immediate, involving, controlled, consistent, and committed. Being consciously present when exploring and making a plan that a student authentically wants for themselves helps with the process.

College students will likely encounter stress and anxiety from time to time and will need support, seeking you out for help. Encouraging students to focus and take action and responsibility for their choices and self-care as well as helping them with strategies and resources—such as mindful strategies—to get through challenging times can aid in enhancing their self-esteem, self-worth, inner peace, and self-confidence. As discussed in previous chapters, to change our thoughts, we need to understand how our mind and brain work, which is associated with the choices we make. There are also strategies that we can use or share with others to help regulate and adjust during difficult times. We must also recognize that at times, despite our best efforts and intentions, we are unfortunately unable to overcome our unwanted thoughts or behavior patterns because they are too deeply ingrained in our mental processes. When you believe a student is at the point that they are unable to work to enhance their well-being, then it is best to refer them to a professional mental health counselor.

REFERENCES

Corey, G. (2017). *Theory and Practice of Counseling and Psychotherapy*. Thompson Brooks/Cole.

Glasser, W. (1972). *Identity Society*. Harper-Collins.

Glasser, W. (1992). Reality therapy. *New York State Journal for Counseling and Development*, 7(1), 5–13.

Glasser, W. (1998). *Choice Theory: A New Psychology of Personal Freedom*. HarperCollins.

Glasser, W. (2001). *Counseling with Choice Theory*. HarperCollins.

Glasser, W. (2008). *Every student can succeed*. Harper-Collins.

Sanford, N. (1962). *The American College*. Wiley.

Sanford, N. (1966). *Self and Society: Social Change and Individual Development*. Atherton.

Wubbolding, R. (1988). *Using Reality Therapy*. HarperCollins.

Wubbolding, R. (1996). Professional issues: The use of questions in reality therapy. *Journal of Reality Therapy*, 16(1), 122–126.

Wubbolding, R. (2000). *Reality Therapy for the 21st Century*. Brunner-Routledge.

Wubbolding, R. (2011). *Reality Therapy*. American Psychological Association.

Wubbolding, R. E. (2015). *Reality Therapy Training Manual* (16th rev.). Center for Reality Therapy.

Wubbolding, R., & Brickell, J. (2009). Perception: The orphaned component of choice theory. *International Journal of Reality Therapy*, 28(2), 50–54.

Chapter 7

Self-Care is the New Health Care

Prescriptions for Well-Being and Being Well

Our health is a valuable asset. It allows us to invest in our talents and passions, to fully participate in our close relationships, to be of service to our community, and to be productive in the workplace. We need energy, endurance, and well-being to carry out our life's purpose. When we are healthy, we are able to invest in our human capital. Furthermore, our health is rooted in our daily routines and habits; therefore, we must be mindful of what we do and the cycle we create when we do what we do.

Because we tend to be overscheduled and often busy with work and life responsibilities, or sometimes in an emotional mindset where we are not motivated to do much, we often put taking care of ourselves on the back burner. Before you know it, this choice can take a toll on us—mentally, emotionally, and physically. Existence in an automatic, nonmindful mode can cause us to refuse to acknowledge or attend to a thought, emotion, motive, or object of perception and disengage us from automatic thoughts, habits, and unhealthy behavior patterns (Brown & Ryan, 2003). Taking time to be "in the present," those mindful moments, has the potential to enhance our attention and focus, as well as improve memory, self-understanding, and self-management skills (Baer, 2010). Mindfulness practice may also be beneficial for enhancing our capacity for attention and concentration, strengthening our ability to accept the present moment, allowing greater self-awareness and compassion, and increasing our capacity for self-regulation (Cashwell, Bentley, and Bigbee, 2007). Considering the potential benefits being in the moment, being aware, being mentally and emotionally fit, and physically well, it would behoove us to engage in behaviors and make choices that promote our self-care.

Self-care is taking the time to be mindful and pay attention to yourself in a way that ensures there is intention to sustain your mental, emotional, and physical health. The idea is that we should not focus on our health only when we are sick but put forth initiative toward maintaining our health consistently. Essentially, self-care is everything we do to deliberately maintain our mental, physical, and emotional well-being. Engaging in self-care can include simple acts, like not checking emails at night before going to sleep, to more purposeful decisions, like going to get a massage. It can be hard to find time to do things for ourselves when we have so much to do and responsibilities. Nonetheless, we have to consider the fact that our "self" goes beyond us, including everyone around us—our families, our friends, our partners, our network, our workplace, and/or our communities. Self-care is deciding to have a healthy relationship with yourself, which can then transfer to your relationships with others.

Self-care is personal, and there is no general rule that will work at all times for everyone. Self-care is about what motivates you (and not others) and what gives you energy. Self-care is about keeping the commitment you make to yourself to focus on you for the short term and the long term. Self-care requires personal initiative, and to some degree, it is a matter of self-help and self-regulation (Moses, Bradley, & O'Callaghan, 2016). In the end, self-care practices are self-initiated activities that maintain and promote our physical and emotional health (Myers et al., 2012), which can include healthy eating, sleeping, stillness, exercising, and engaging with your surroundings and others.

A STUDENT'S VOICE

When I was in my freshman year of college, I wish someone would have told me that self-care is needed because college is hard. I overworked myself with coursework and full-time work. I was stressed and hated college after my first semester. One thing I wish my parents would have done for me is make sure I could cook basic meals before I left the house for college. I always made the excuse to come home because I was tired of eating campus food. I built bad eating habits because I never cooked in my dorm. This stressed me out because I was trying to avoid the "freshman 15." I was into body image my freshman year and this affected me. I'm a better cook now; however, I wish I had known how my freshman year.

—A 22-year-old graduate student

THE FIVE DOCTORS: GET YOUR PRESCRIPTION

Our bodies constantly organize and carry out intricate operations to maintain our health and well-being. The "pharmacy" that exists within each of us benefits from the food we eat; the amount of physical activity, sleep, and stillness we get; and our intake amount of fresh air and sunshine. These prescriptions allow us to come a little closer to ourselves. As humans, we are always in a position of choice and are able to regulate ourselves, and while we cannot control the weather or our genetics, we can control what we do every day. We have moment-to-moment choices. This "pharmacy" within also reminds us that nothing outside of ourselves can make us better without a partnership with what's inside of us. In this awareness, we are reminded that life is sacred; each one of us is sacred. We can ask ourselves if our sacred temple, that is our body, is clean. When it comes to our body's wellness, our overall wellness, how we do anything is how we do everything. Our signature is everywhere.

It has been said that 1 hour of health is 23 hours of freedom. We must do at least one thing towards health, longevity, and vitality each day; we must have a daily routine. A part of this goal can be derived from the five doctors of Nature, Sleep, Food, Exercise, and Stillness. Details for each are presented below in a manner for you to easily convey to students how they can always count down 5, 4, 3, 2, 1—e.g., 5 simple ways to connect with nature, 4 better sleep habits, 3 ways to let food be their medicine, 2 exercise hacks, and 1 radical act of sanity. Subsequently, you can encourage students to find their medicine and use it.

Dr. Nature

Being outside in the outdoor natural environments—such as walking trails, forests, seaside, countryside, parks, meadows, fields, canyons, mountains, green areas, and gardens—has benefits for our physical and mental health. Being in touch with nature has benefits such as reducing the risk of illnesses involving chronic stress, promoting a range of intermediate outcomes such as increased subjective well-being, and possibly having a physical influence for certain types of activities (e.g., walking, biking, and outdoor play) (Hartig, Mitchell, de Vries, & Frumkin, 2014). As well, viewing nature and natural scenes is a pleasurable experience (Biederman & Vessel, 2006), much better than looking at walls, asphalt, and concrete. Exposure to nature not only makes us feel better emotionally, it also contributes to our physical well-being and restores us.

Furthermore, green exercise—exercise in the presence of nature—can lead to positive short and long-term health outcomes. Exposure to a green environment during exercise can lead to improved self-esteem and mood, particularly when there is a presence of water, as a green environment provides an important health service (Barton & Pretty, 2010). Being in outdoor natural environments "may provide some of the best all-round health benefits by increasing physical activity levels with lower levels of perceived exertion, altering physiological functioning including stress reduction, restoring mental fatigue, and improving mood and self-esteem and perceived health" (Gladwell et al., 2013, p. 5). Green exercise is a way to disconnect so that we can boost the mind–body benefits of our workouts and simultaneously reap the benefits of nature.

For college students, taking a break and getting outside for at least a few minutes is good for their self-care. Outdoor spaces should be seen as more than merely transitions from one building to the next, but rather as a place to restore. Some institutions of higher education offer outdoor programs that provide outdoor recreation and sports for students. Getting away from the laptop, cell phone, television, and the "indoors" to a natural setting can positively impact their well-being. College students' integration of outdoor time into their schedule can bring forth physical and mental benefits, which can contribute to their success in college.

We must encourage our students to "go look at a tree," and allow them to be in communication with the natural world of dragonflies, hummingbirds, the wind, or a rainbow. When they are constantly indoors, they do not get to an understanding of living with and respecting the rhythms of nature. Being outdoors shows a student that everything they need is already within them; just as nature has everything she needs to sustain and grow, so do they.

Five Simple Ways to Connect with Nature

1. Stargaze: Choose to sit or lie on a blanket outside on a cloudless night. The farther from city lights, the better. Take a moment to admire the universe and to be humbly reminded of our life here on an Earth that is a part of an enormous universe.
2. Place Bond: When outside, notice the natural structures and aesthetics, things that are not man made. Allow yourself to be aware of any bushes, trees, or rocks that are around. Notice if your attention is drawn to anything more than another and then find a spot to "sit near" what you are drawn to.
3. Go Earthing/Grounding: Just as the sun gives us warmth and vitamin D, the earth touching our bare feet gives us balanced energy. The earth is rich in nutrients but also has a beneficial negative energy that we can connect with to counter the positive charge from our busy modern lifestyles.
4. Visit Water: On average, we are made up of approximately 67% water. Water is also the fundamental basis of all life on planet Earth. Time near or in natural water can be soothing and energizing to the soul. Take a visit with any body of water for at least a few minutes and notice the feeling or mood within.

5. Heart to Earth: Touch the earth with one hand and touch your heart with the other hand, and then, just be. Placing a hand on the heart creates a softening, while placing the other hand on the earth is grounding and connecting to nature and its natural healing intelligence.

Dr. Sleep

Sleep is essential to good physical and mental health and is a foundation for our well-being and functioning. When we sleep, our bodies work to take care of vital functions, and thus, regularly getting adequate amounts of sleep can have profound effects on our body's self-regulation and maintenance. Our ability to function and feel well while awake depends on whether we get enough total sleep and enough of each type of sleep—rapid eye movement (REM) and non-REM that occur in a regular pattern of between three and five cycles each night—and on whether we sleep at a time our bodies are prepared to sleep (NIH, n.d.). If we do not get enough sleep (e.g., sleep homeostasis), are sleeping at the wrong times (being out of sync with your circadian rhythm), or have poor quality sleep, it is likely that we will awaken not feeling refreshed and alert and feeling very tired during the day. Getting enough quality sleep at the right times can help protect mental health, physical health, quality of life, and well-being.

When we do not get quality sleep, there are short-term and long-term consequences. Sleep deficiency, which includes sleep deprivation, occurs when sleep is insufficient in quantity or quality for optimal health and performance, and may result from inadequate total sleep duration or from fragmentation of sleep (NIH, n.d.). Sleep deficiency can interfere with quality of life, daily functioning, and feelings of well-being and can lead to physical and mental health problems, injuries, loss of productivity, impairment of the body's immune system, and harm to emotional stability and cognitive functions. Sleep medicine and its study has grown into a multidisciplinary field and now includes the wisdom and investigations of dentists, cardiologists, neurologists, psychiatrists, cardiologists, respiratory physicians, and ear, throat, and nose doctors, just to name a few.

Considering the possible consequences of not getting an adequate amount of sleep, college students, who are known for variable sleep schedules, can face problems that impact their success in college. For example, lack of sleep can affect their memory, their ability to focus and concentrate, and the quality of their coursework (Orzech, Salafsky, & Hamilton, 2011), which impedes their academic performance. In addition, a student's perceived stress and negative mood, including anger, confusion, depression, and tension, are connected to poor quality sleep (Lund Reiter, Whiting, & Pritchard, 2010). Therefore, for college students' welfare and success in college, self-care includes them getting a proper amount of sleep (Hirshkowitz et al., 2015).

What is the "proper" amount of sleep for a college student? Researchers have come to understand that "proper" or normal sleep requirements depend on a person's genes as well as the quality of sleep (Leschziner, 2019). Neurologist and sleep physician Guy Leschziner describes the right amount of sleep as the number of hours needed to wake up refreshed, without daytime sleepiness and being ready for bed at a regular time with no difficulty falling asleep. When students are mindful and aware of themselves, they are better able to know their own, unique sleep prescription.

Four Tips for Better Sleep

1. Nose breathing: Wholesome sleep is mouth-shut sleep. Insomnia, long to be perceived as a psychological problem, is often a breathing problem (Nestor, 2020). Many people cannot sleep because they cannot breathe. Healthy nostril breathing, where they open and close like flowers throughout the day and night, is a crucial act for peaceful rest. Even if it requires a thin strip of tape to keep the mouth closed (a funny and current practice done by the first author, Dr. Dye) to stay mouth-breathing free during sleep.
2. Unplug: At least one hour before bed, unplug and detach yourself from all devices. Allow the mind and body to prepare for rest without the screen of computers, phones, and televisions.
3. Routine: Create a simple and flexible bedtime routine. A nice walk after dinner, a warm shower to wash off the day, or some simple breath work to let go of the day can be a part of a healthy bedtime practice.
4. Wake with Gratitude: First, a well-rested body sets the tone for the day. After you awake and before you get out of bed, allow yourself to wake with a gratitude of the day. Allow yourself to become aware of who you truly are and your connection with life. Take a moment to connect with the thought of a new day, perhaps look at something auspicious, and notice the space between the inhale and exhale.

Dr. Food

Eating is one of the core components of self-care because food nurtures our bodies. Considering the essential nature of food and water to our existence, what, when, and how we eat is connected to our health. Nourishment of our bodies is a foundation of our health and well-being.

Unfortunately, we sometimes can become so engrossed in our days that we eat as fast as possible between tasks on the to-do list and errands; grab high-calorie, high-fat, processed, and low-nutrient food that is quick to access; get too busy at work to stop and eat; or avoid eating to lose weight. Sometimes, taking time out of our day to prepare "healthy" foods can become a nuisance and even costly, and it can be easier to stop by a fast-food restaurant or warm up a highly processed dish, especially when we feel tired.

For college students, food choice is often dictated by the options that surround them (e.g., all-you-can-eat facilities and fast-food restaurants). Additionally, students tend to choose food according to taste preference (Abraham, Noriega Brooke, & Shin, 2018). Students having proper nutrition is necessary as there is a link between the quality of diet and psychological disorders such as anxiety and depression (Jacka, Mykletun, & Berk, 2012). Students may have a fair knowledge of nutritional requirements for their health; however, food choices they make can be not necessarily healthy and can lead to inadequate nutrition, which can affect students' health and academic success (Abraham, Noriega Brooke, & Shin, 2018). College students with food insecurity, being without reliable access to a sufficient quantity of affordable, nutritious food, are also at risk of health and academic problems (Payne-Sturges et al., 2018). Considering the physical and mental deficits associated with poor nutrition for college students (e.g., stress, tiredness, and lack of focus and motivation), it is imperative that college students eat nutritional foods for their daily health and well-being.

Healthy eating is a preventative approach to health. We should let our food be our medicine and our medicine be our food. Ayurveda, an ancient holistic medical system of India, identifies natural foods as primary in healthy eating and sustaining good health. This ancient system and its principles are accessible to all. Students can learn to use natural wellness practices like Ayurvedic eating to develop a more healing and healthy diet.

Three Ways to Let Your Food Be Your Medicine and Your Medicine Be Your Food

1. Take in foods closest to their original, natural state.

   When we eat foods closest to how they grew in nature, we are better able to access nature and the natural intelligence and energy of the food. This natural intelligence is in the form of vitamins, minerals, fiber, and healthy fats that provide the body with everything it needs. The food's energy changes and is often depleted when processed out of its natural state.

2. Keep inflammation in the body low with superfoods.

   Most superfoods are great at supporting and enhancing healthy digestion. A strong digestion equals properly metabolized food. Here is a list of foods considered to be pure, energizing, and life-giving:
   - Seeds, oils, and raw nuts: Help promote a healthy cardiovascular system, are full of nutrients, and help lubricate and improve the digestive tract.

- Ginger: Helps to reduce inflammation and serves as an excellent digestive aid, including other varied health benefits.
- Turmeric: An anti-inflammatory and powerful medicinal spice than can help balance the whole person physically and mentally.
- Honey: Helps to boost immunity and increase energy. It is also an excellent alternative to sugar. However, avoid cooking with and heating up honey as this decreases its nutritional benefits.

3. Practice local, now, and grow.

When possible, purchase fresh fruits, vegetables, and herbs locally. Support local growers by visiting the local farmers' market, and if a local farmers' market is not available, choose to shop around the perimeter of the grocery store. Fresh foods are usually kept around the perimeter of grocery stores.

Choose to eat fruits and vegetables that are in season. This practice helps you to avoid exposure to nonorganic, preserving chemicals that may be used for shipping.

Grow your own. The process of creating a small garden is easier than one thinks. Even if it is only a few herbs or a tomato plant, dirt, water, seeds, and sun can be magical. Growing your own allows you to witness firsthand the energizing magic of the sun, dirt, and water that make food so energizing. Food has energy and is energy.

Dr. Exercise

For many of us, our lives are so full that we are not sure how we can add exercise into full days. When we do think of incorporating exercise into our routines, we might have questions such as: When will I have the time to start and maintain an exercise routine with my busy schedule? What task or responsibility will I have to sacrifice in lieu of exercising? What is the best type of exercise for me and how long do I need to exercise to be effective? Where do I start? Having questions and concerns is understandable, but what is undeniable is that regular exercise is one of the best things you can do for your health.

Physical activity is defined as any bodily movement produced by skeletal muscles that results in energy expenditure; in daily life, this can be categorized into occupational, sports, conditioning, household, or other activities. Exercise, a subset of physical activity, is planned, structured, and repetitive with a final or an intermediate objective of improvement or maintenance of physical fitness (Caspersen, Powell, & Christenson, 1985). An abundance of research has shown that physical activity, which includes exercise, has beneficial outcomes. Generally, those who engage in regular physical activity display more desirable health outcomes across a variety of physical conditions, which are associated with better quality of life and health outcomes (Penedo & Dahn, 2005). These benefits include to improve mood and mental health, increase energy, promote better sleep, ramp up metabolism for weight loss and maintenance, and contribute to prevention or management of a wide range of health problems and concerns, such as high blood pressure, heart disease, diabetes, and depression (Mayo Clinic, 2019; Warburton, Nicol, & Bredin, 2006). In addition, exercise can improve mental health, including improving mood; reducing symptoms of stress, anger, and depression; alleviating anxiety; and slowing cognitive decline (Babyak et al., 2000).

According to the World Health Organization (2011), adults aged 18–64 should do "at least 150 minutes of moderate-intensity aerobic physical activity throughout the week or do at least 75 minutes of vigorous-intensity aerobic physical activity throughout the week or an equivalent combination of moderate- and vigorous-intensity activity" (para. 4), which can be accomplished in multiple ways (e.g., shorter bouts of 10 minutes spread throughout the week or 30 minutes of moderate intensity five times per week).

Two Tried and True Exercise Tips

1. Do what you like. Find out what type of movement you enjoy and do it. If you do not know what you enjoy, then make a game of trying out new things. Most universities that have fitness facilities host a variety of classes. Try Zumba or kickboxing for two weeks. If you do not enjoy that, try swimming or the treadmill. Exercise is not one size fits all, and it does not have to be done in only one way. Have fun, and experiment with types of exercise that fit your personal, social, physical, mental, and spiritual needs.
2. Find inspiration. Ask yourself what is your *why?* Why do you want to exercise? Perhaps you want to change your physical appearance or want to lower your blood pressure. Some people join groups for inspiration or to prepare for a competition for inspiration. Connect to your why and use it to inspire you.

Dr. Stillness

Some of us awaken and hit the ground running in the morning and hit the bed exhausted at night. In between awakening and bedtime, our days are filled with duties, responsibilities, deadlines, and errands. Being busy, overscheduled, and constantly in action can present a significant problem for us when it comes to our health and well-being. Thus, having downtime and stillness is essential for our restoration. However, we are often so intertwined in our thoughts, feelings, and tasks that a few moments of nothing—no calls, no texting, no shopping, no talking to family and friends, no social media, no television, no videos, no music—seem impossible. We can struggle to be still.

Stillness starts in the mind. Stillness, pausing activities and resting our minds, is important in developing self-control and self-regulation (Gillen & Gillen, 2007). Stillness, in a broad way, extends beyond all perceptions, thoughts, and feelings and encompasses an absence of sensory experience and emotion (Meares, 1977; Pearson, 2013). Stillness—physical, mental, and spiritual—although not easy, can be helpful to us in the midst of chaos (Holiday, 2019). In these situations in which we navigate crises, we must "be fully present; empty our mind of preconceptions; take our time; sit quietly and reflect; reject distraction; weigh advice against the counsel of our convictions; and deliberate without being paralyzed" (Holiday, 2019, p. 21). Properly channeled, stillness can be used to quieten racing thoughts and route brain waves into a calmed, harmonious state.

College students taking the time to simply be still for a part of their day, even for a short period of time, can make a difference in how they manage their day. As college students tend to have busy schedules, learning how to sit in stillness while attending to the many complex workings of the mind and body is like a radical act of sanity. It is a way to experience the love of life and the present moment. The awareness gained in stillness allows us to want to be in a right relationship with ourselves.

One Radical Act of Sanity

1. Even if just for 5 minutes a day or 60 seconds at a time, notice the breath and you can become more even minded. A sense of peace comes when you sit with you. As you practice stillness more, you can then carry your stillness with you everywhere you go so that the chaos of life does not overshadow you.

TAKE A MOMENT

Take a brief moment and ask yourself or others the following questions.

- What would be an impetus for me to create a self-care plan for myself?
- Do I need the support of a community to help me with my self-care plan, or do I feel comfortable learning and doing it on my own?
- What other activities or practices have I committed to in my life? How can I use lessons from these experiences to help me with adhering to my self-care plan?

- If I am feeling down, what do I like to do to cheer myself up? How would I describe my ideal day?
- Do I usually give myself the time needed to recharge before I feel depleted or do I wait until I feel depleted before taking time to care for myself? Why do I choose to recharge in this manner?
- What have I done to be kind to myself this year?
- What efforts do I take to integrate my responsibilities, work, and life expectations in way where I feel some sense of balance?

MAKING A PLAN

Just as there is more than one way to do things, there is no one formula for self-care. The goal is to respect your needs and listen to your mind and body. You will need to self-reflect on what areas of your life need more of your attention and time.

As self-care is associated with positive physical health, emotional well-being, and mental health (Cook-Cottone & Guyker, 2018), it plays an important role in maintaining and promoting physical and emotional well-being. Therefore, to maintain a healthy relationship with ourselves so that we can manage our lives in a way that is healthy and productive, we need to engage in self-care. Once an individual has decided to engage in self-care, the first task can be to make a plan.

Mindful self-care, a set of practices that support positive embodiment and a way of inhabiting the body, is an iterative process that involves mindful awareness and assessment of our internal needs and external demands and an intentional engagement in specific practices of self-care to address needs and demands in a manner that serves our well-being and personal effectiveness (Cook-Cottone, 2015). The following assessment, worksheets, and planning forms (for the day or for the week) can help you brainstorm, assess, and develop a plan and pathway to self-care, well-being, and being well.

SELF-CARE ASSESSMENT

Below is a series of statements about how you view and navigate daily as well as your internal needs and external demands that may affect your self-care practice. Each statement has two options on opposing sides. After reading each of the statements, select the degree to which option **best describes you.**

I tend to wake up every morning with a sense of gratitude.						I wake up every morning bracing myself for a day filled with problems.
☐	☐	☐	☐	☐	☐	☐

I typically think about the good things in my life throughout the day.						I typically ruminate on problems and conflicts.
☐	☐	☐	☐	☐	☐	☐

I typically strive to consciously discard hard feelings.						I often harbor and focus on resentments.
☐	☐	☐	☐	☐	☐	☐

I typically tend to stay focused throughout the day.						I typically tend to lose focus as my mind wanders throughout the day.
☐	☐	☐	☐	☐	☐	☐

(Continued)

135

I feel equipped to handle most of life's challenges most of the time.

I feel like life is overwhelming and I am not equipped to deal with its challenges most of the time.

☐   ☐   ☐   ☐   ☐   ☐   ☐

I am often aware of my surroundings.

I tend to move aimlessly throughout my day with minimal awareness of my surroundings.

☐   ☐   ☐   ☐   ☐   ☐   ☐

I typically speak kindly to myself

I often engage in negative self-talk.

☐   ☐   ☐   ☐   ☐   ☐   ☐

I tend to drink water throughout the day.

I tend to drink beverages (e.g., juice, coffee, or soda) throughout the day.

☐   ☐   ☐   ☐   ☐   ☐   ☐

I am energized to exercise at least 20 minutes per day.

I do not know how I can fit at least 20 minutes of exercise into my day.

☐   ☐   ☐   ☐   ☐   ☐   ☐

(*Continued*)

I tend to eat more healthy foods (e.g., leafy greens, unprocessed foods, fruit, and low sodium foods) throughout the week.

I tend to eat more unhealthy food (e.g., processed foods, sugary foods, and high sodium foods) throughout the week.

☐　　☐　　☐　　☐　　☐　　☐　　☐

I tend to eat smaller meals throughout the course of the day.

I tend to be so busy that I skip meals and eat one big meal during the day.

☐　　☐　　☐　　☐　　☐　　☐　　☐

I tend to snack deliberately most of the time.

I tend to snack mindlessly most of the time.

☐　　☐　　☐　　☐　　☐　　☐　　☐

I typically sleep at least 7 hours or more per week.

I typically sleep 6 or less hours per week.

☐　　☐　　☐　　☐　　☐　　☐　　☐

(*Continued*)

I typically get regular preventative medical examinations and check-ups.

I rarely get a chance to regularly get preventative medical examinations.

☐ ☐ ☐ ☐ ☐ ☐ ☐

I tend to take time to get away when I feel the need.

I tend to not take time to get away because I do not want to get behind on what I think that I need to do.

☐ ☐ ☐ ☐ ☐ ☐ ☐

I tend to balance myself.

I tend to overexert myself.

☐ ☐ ☐ ☐ ☐ ☐ ☐

I cope well with stress.

I allow stress to consume my day most of the time.

☐ ☐ ☐ ☐ ☐ ☐ ☐

(Continued)

I typically take action to reduce stress when I notice the signs.						I ignore the signs of stress because I have to keep moving forward.
☐	☐	☐	☐	☐	☐	☐

I often feel that I am on top of things.						I often feel that things are piling up on top of me.
☐	☐	☐	☐	☐	☐	☐

I have at least one person to whom I can turn for support and affection regularly.						I do not have anyone to who I can turn for support and affection regularly.
☐	☐	☐	☐	☐	☐	☐

I typically take quiet time for myself during the day and engage in activities to promote relaxation/ mindfulness.						I do not take quiet time for myself during the day and engage in activities to promote relaxation/ mindfulness.
☐	☐	☐	☐	☐	☐	☐

After reviewing your responses, what intentions would you set for your self-care?

What, if any, of your current practices do you wish to change?

What, if any, barriers do you have to your self-care?

SELF-CARE BRAINSTORM

My Intention
How do I want to show up each day this week?

My Commitment
What will I commit to this week?

1 **My Body**
What can I do this week to nurture my body and attend to its needs?

② **My Mind**

What will help me be aware, purposeful, and intellectually engaged this week?

③ **My Emotions**

What ways can I use my thoughts and feelings to better serve me this week?

④ **My Spirit**

What can I do this week to connect to my true self?

WRITE A DAILY PRESCRIPTION FOR YOUR SELF-CARE AND WELL-BEING

Make "your prescription" for the day unique to you, your interests, your availability, and your abilities. What you choose can include small tasks such as taking a step outside to take a deep breath to something that requires a little more time out of your day, like going to get a massage. Choose as many areas that you believe you can handle for the day. Try to write the prescription the night before so that you can view it and start "your prescription" when you start your day. The prescription below is an example.

℞

Name: Clara

Date: 12/14

Thoughts: I will name one thing I am grateful for before I get out of bed.

Water: I will drink at least 6 glasses of water (8 ounces per glass).

Food: I will drink a green smoothie.

Movement: I will take a 30 minute walk after work and before dinner.

Sleep: I will turn off all electronic devices at least 30 mins before bedtime.

Now, take a moment and write your prescription for the day.

℞

Name: _____

Date: _____

My Self-Care Plan

Week of_____

	Physical	Mental	Nutrition	Rest/Stillness	Cognitive
Sunday					
Monday					
Tuesday					
Wednesday					
Thursday					
Friday					
Saturday					

In developing your self-care plan, listen to your mind and body. Think about what you value. Next, identify what you currently need. What activities are within your comfort level and are of interest to you?

In creating your plan, think about how you can embed these activities in your daily or weekly routine. Do what feels comfortable to you. If you need to start small, do so. You do not have to assign a task to yourself for each day.

Ideas for a Self-Care Plan

 Physical
- Walk at least 20 minutes on a treadmill or outside
- Take a hike on a trail
- Practice yoga
- Go to the gym for an hour
- Get quality sleep

 Mental
- Journaling
- Wake up and say one thing I am grateful for today
- Breathwork
- Compliment one person today
- Engage in an act of kindness
- Tackle one small step to accomplish something I have been avoiding

 Rest/Stillness
- Meditate
- Find a quiet place and repeat calming phrases
- Take time to take at least a 30-minute break during the day to relax
- Take a nap
- Light a candle and cozy up with a soft blanket

 Nutrition
- Take multi-vitamins
- Drink water
- Select fresh vegetables as a side for a meal
- Eat fresh fruit
- Eat gut-friendly foods for snacks, like natural yogurt, walnuts, almonds, or oat bran

 Cognitive
- Learn something new about an interest or a hobby
- Coloring
- Play a game you enjoy (e.g., Solitaire or Word games)
- Read a few pages of something you enjoy (e.g., a book, poetry, or affirmations)

SELF-CARE AND THE COLLEGE STUDENT

For college students, it can be especially important to engage in self-care, considering the daily routines, expectations, and responsibilities (of course, to varying degrees) that accompany being a college student. The relationships between psychological adjustment and mindful acceptance, sleep hygiene, and social support and nonsignificant effects associated with mindful awareness and physical activity (Myers et al., 2012) are important for college students to understand. So, when we talk about helping college students relieve anxiety and stress, we should help them understand these connections and include the idea of having a plan to maintain their well-being beyond merely getting through those moments of anxiety and stress.

The need for self-care behaviors which are built in emerging adulthood, such as during the college years, provides the foundation for long-term health as well (Viner & Baker, 2005). As such, students must become aware of their self-care needs and must initiate strategies for meeting these needs (Turner et al., 2005). But because many students cannot, or will not, initiate strategies for meeting their self-care needs alone, self-care practices need to be enabled, demonstrated, and encouraged by others (Moses, J., Bradley, G. L., & O'Callaghan, 2016). Fundamentally, higher education professionals can encourage students to create a self-care plan and explain the benefits of their use. Higher education professionals should be urged to continue to offer education, advice, and evidence-based interventions that promote self-care practices to college students.

REFERENCES

Abraham, S., Noriega Brooke, R., & Shin, J. Y. (2018). College students' eating habits and knowledge of nutritional requirements. *Journal of Nutrition and Human Health*, *2*(1), 13–17. https://doi.org/10.35841/nutrition-human-health.2.1.13-17

Babyak, M., Blumenthal, J. A., Herman, S., Khatri, P., Doraiswamy, M., Moore, K., ... Krishnan, K. R. (2000). Exercise treatment for major depression: Maintenance of therapeutic benefit at 10 months. *Psychosomatic Medicine*, *62*, 633–638. https://doi.org/10.1097/00006842-200009000-00006

Baer, R. (2010). *Assessing Mindfulness and Acceptance Processes in Clients: Illuminating the Theory and Practice of Change*. New Harbinger Publications.

Barton, J., & Pretty, J. (2010). What is the best dose of nature and green exercise for improving mental health? A multi-study analysis. *Environmental Science & Technology*, *44*(10), 3947–3955. https://doi.org/10.1021/es903183r

Biederman, I., & Vessel, E. A. (2006). Perceptual pleasure and the brain. *American Scientist*, *94*, 247–253. https://doi.org/10.1511/2006.59.247

Brown, K. W., & Ryan, R. M. (2003). The benefits of being present: Mindfulness and its role in psychological well-being. *Journal of Personality and Social Psychology*, *84*, 822–848. http://dx.doi.org/10.1037/0022-3514.84.4.822

Cashwell, C. S., Bentley, D. P., & Bigbee, A. (2007). Spirituality and counselor wellness. *The Journal of Humanistic Counseling*, *46*(1), 66–81. https://doi.org/10.1002/j.2161-1939.2007.tb00026.x

Caspersen, C. J., Powell, K. E., & Christenson, G. M. (1985). Physical activity, exercise, and physical fitness: Definitions and distinctions for health-related research. *Public Health Reports (Washington, D.C., 1974)*, *100*(2), 126–131.

Cook-Cottone, C. P. (2015). Incorporating positive body image into the treatment of eating disorders: A model for attunement and mindful self-care. *Body Image*, *14*, 158–167. https://doi:10.1016/j.bodyim.2015.03.004

Cook-Cottone, C. P., & Guyker, W. M. (2018). The development and validation of the Mindful Self-Care Scale (MSCS): An assessment of practices that support positive embodiment. *Mindfulness*, *9*(1), 161–175. https://doi.org/10.1007/s12671-017-0759-1

Gillen, L., & Gillen, J. (2007). *Yoga Calm for Children: Educating Heart, Mind, and Body*. Three Pebble Press.

Gladwell, V. F., Brown, D. K., Wood, C., Sandercock, G. R., & Barton, J. L. (2013). The great outdoors: How a green exercise environment can benefit all. *Extreme Physiology & Medicine*, *2*(1), 3. https://doi.org/10.1186/2046-7648-2-3

Hartig, T., Mitchell, R., de Vries, S., & Frumkin, H. (2014). Nature and health. *Annual Review of Public Health*, *35*, 207–228. https://doi.org/10.1146/annurev-publhealth-032013-182443

Hirshkowitz, M., Whiton, K., Albert, S. M., Alessi, C., Bruni, O., DonCarlos, L., ... Hillard, P. J. A. (2015). National Sleep Foundation's sleep time duration recommendations: Methodology and results summary. *Sleep Health*, *1*(1), 40–43. http://dx.doi.org/10.1016/j.sleh.2014.12.010

Holiday, R. (2019). *Stillness is the Key*. Portfolio/Penguin.

Jacka, F. N., Mykletun, A., & Berk, M. (2012). Moving towards a population health approach to the primary prevention of common mental disorders. *BioMed Central Medicine*, *10*, 149. https://doi.org/10.1186/1741-7015-10-149

Leschziner, G. (2019). *The Nocturnal Brain*. St. Martin's Publishing Group.

Lund, H. G., Reider, B. D., Whiting, A. B., & Pritchard, J. R. (2010). Sleep patterns and predictors of disturbed sleep in a large population of college students. *Journal of Adolescent Health*, *46*, 124–132. https://doi.org/10.1016/j.jadohealth.2009.06.016

Mayo Clinic Staff. (2019, May 11). *Exercise: 7 Benefits of Regular Physical Activity*. Retrieved from https://www.mayoclinic.org/healthy-lifestyle/fitness/in-depth/exercise/art-20048389

Meares, A. (1977). The quality of meditation effective in the regression of cancer. *The Journal of the American Society of Psychosomatic Dentistry and Medicine*, *25*, 129–132.

Moses, J., Bradley, G. L., & O'Callaghan, F. V. (2016). When college students look after themselves: Self-care practices and well-being. *Journal of Student Affairs Research and Practice*, *53*(3), 346–359.

Myers, S. B., Sweeney, A. C., Popick, V., Wesley, K., Bordfeld, A., & Fingerhut, R. (2012). Self-care practices and perceived stress levels among psychology graduate students. *Training and Education in Professional Psychology*, *6*(1), 55–66. https://doi:10.1037/a0026534

National Institutes of Health (n.d.). *Sleep Deprivation and Deficiency*. Retrieved from https://www.nhlbi.nih.gov/health-topics/sleep-deprivation-and-deficiency

Nestor, J. (2020). *Breath. The New Science of a Lost Art*. Riverhead Books.

Orzech, K. M., Salafsky, D. B., & Hamilton, L. (2011). The state of sleep among college students at a large public university. *Journal of American College Health*, *59*(7), 612–619. https://doi.org/10.1080/07448481.2010.520051

Payne-Sturges, D. C., Tjaden, A., Caldeira, K. M., Vincent, K. B., & Arria, A. M. (2018). Student hunger on campus: Food insecurity among college students and implications for academic institutions. *American Journal of Health Promotion*, *32*(2), 349–354. https://doi.org/10.1177/0890117117719620

Pearson, C. (2013). *The Supreme Awakening: Experiences of Enlightenment Throughout Time—And How You Can Cultivate Them*. Maharishi University of Management Press.

Penedo, F., & Dahn, J. (2005). Exercise and well-being: A review of mental and physical health benefits associated with physical activity. *Current Opinion in Psychiatry*, *18*(2), 189–193. https://doi.org/10.1097/00001504-200503000-00013

Turner, J. A., Edwards, L. M., Eicken, I. M., Yokoyama, K., Castro, J. R., Tran, A.-N., & Haggins, K. L. (2005). Intern self-care: An exploratory study into strategy use and effectiveness. *Professional Psychology: Research and Practice*, *36*(6), 674–680. https://doi.org/10.1037/0735-7028.36.6.674

Viner, R. M., & Barker, M. (2005). Young people's health: The need for action. *British Medical Journal*, *330*(7496), 901–903. https://doi.org/10.1136/bmj.330.7496.901

Warburton, D. E., Nicol, C. W., & Bredin, S. S. (2006). Health benefits of physical activity: The evidence. *CMAJ: Canadian Medical Association Journal*, *174*(6), 801–809. https://doi.org/10.1503/cmaj.051351

World Health Organization. (2011). *Global Recommendations on Physical Activity for Health*. Retrieved from https://www.who.int/dietphysicalactivity/physical-activity-recommendations-18-64years.pdf?ua=1

Index

adults 1, 3, 23, 34, 36, 41–42, 50–51,
107, 109, 132
anxiety 2–4, 6–8, 16, 26, 56, 58, 67, 69,
93, 112, 122, 130, 146
awareness 4, 5, 8, 13, 16, 18–19, 23, 34,
44, 53, 60, 64–66, 68, 77, 80–83, 86,
87, 91–96, 98–99, 103, 105, 114, 116,
119, 121, 124, 126, 133–134, 136, 146

behavior(s) 1, 10, 13–14, 16, 19, 24,
26, 27, 31–32, 36–38, 40–42, 64,
88–89, 105–106, 110–116, 119–122,
124, 146
body 1–4, 6–9, 11, 13–14, 16–18, 23,
25, 32–34, 36, 39–41, 43, 45, 48,
52–55, 57–60, 62, 64–69, 71–77,
80–81, 83–87, 91–96, 98–100, 102,
104–105, 107, 125–130, 133–134,
141, 144
brain 5–6, 9, 12, 14, 19, 21, 24–25, 29,
30–33, 35–36, 38, 40–45, 47–49,
51–52, 54–55, 57–58, 60, 63–64, 67,
71, 79, 80, 89, 105, 112, 122, 133
breath 7, 17–18, 32–33, 44–46, 51,
53–55, 60–64, 66–69, 70–79, 80–89,
91–99, 100, 109, 129, 133, 143, 145

choice theory 110–112, 120
college 1–4, 6, 10–13, 18, 23–24,
26–27, 31, 33–34, 36–37, 41–42,
52, 64, 66–67, 70, 90, 105–106,
108–109, 112, 116, 121–122, 125,
127–130, 133, 146
color 3, 12–14, 16, 25, 27, 83, 145
community 1–2, 4, 9–11, 19, 20, 90, 133
connection 1–2, 4, 6–12, 16, 17, 19,
20–23, 30–31, 44, 48, 55, 66, 71, 82,
86, 118, 129

emotions 1, 3, 6, 10–13, 16, 26, 34, 36,
38, 42, 48, 56–60, 64–65, 67, 69,
78–79, 83–84, 91–92, 95, 99, 110,
120–121, 142
energy 2, 4–5, 8, 11–13, 17, 19, 52,
54, 57, 59, 64, 68, 71–72, 75–76,
79, 81–82, 84–85, 87–88, 92, 93,
95–96, 99, 105, 116, 122, 124–125,
127, 130–132
environment 1–4, 8, 10–14, 16–18, 23,
25–27, 34, 38, 42–43, 50, 60, 62, 82,
105, 109, 112, 116, 126, 146

higher education 1–2, 4, 8, 16, 18, 23, 27,
29, 31, 37, 40, 42, 48, 52, 60, 64, 69,
105, 109, 110, 115, 118–119, 127, 146
hormones 7, 34, 38, 40, 54, 86;
adrenaline 52, 54–55; cortisol 7,
40, 54–55, 63; dopamine 40, 86;
endorphin 38, 40; oxytocin 38, 40,
86; serotonin 12, 27, 40, 86

light 12–13, 21, 24–26, 84, 88, 93, 127, 145
loneliness 6, 9–10, 25

meditation 12, 16–19, 65–70, 88–89
mental health 1–4, 9, 10, 16, 24–52, 121–122, 126, 128, 132, 134, 146
mind 1–9, 11–12, 14, 16–19, 23–27, 31, 45, 48–49, 52–54, 57, 59–61, 64–70, 73, 76, 79–87, 91–93, 105–106, 111, 122, 127, 129, 133–135, 142, 144; mindfulness 2, 4, 7, 16–19, 23–26, 51, 53, 57, 59, 62–63, 65–67, 69, 70, 88–89, 91–93, 120–121, 124, 139, 146
mood 7, 12–14, 24–27, 38, 40, 42, 56–57, 77, 121, 126–128, 132

nature 9, 11, 14, 17, 31, 67, 84–85, 88, 126–130, 146
neuroplasticity 5, 30–31, 48

physical 1–4, 7–8, 10, 12, 17–20, 22–23, 26–27, 29–31, 33, 40, 48, 51, 55, 60, 64, 72, 75, 90–92, 98, 100, 107, 109, 110, 120, 124–128, 130–133, 144
physiological 7, 10, 14, 26, 54–55, 66, 75, 110, 127
plants 14, 26–27
practice 12, 18–22, 24–25, 43–47, 51, 57–70, 73–75, 77, 89, 91–96, 102–103, 105, 118, 120–122, 124–125, 130–131, 133–135, 140, 145
prefrontal cortex 40–42, 47, 49, 63–64, 67

psychological 1–3, 7, 11, 13, 19, 23–26, 40, 50–51, 53–54, 72, 89, 109–110, 120, 123, 129, 130, 146

racial 3, 24
relationships 1–3, 9, 17, 27, 29, 31, 49, 106, 118, 122, 125, 146
relaxation 16, 19, 60, 64, 68, 86, 93

self-awareness 19, 23, 66, 93–95, 124
self-care 2, 66, 121–122, 124–125, 128–129, 133–135, 140–141, 143
sleep 12–13, 17, 34–35, 52, 66, 86, 125–126, 128–129, 132, 137, 145
social 1, 2, 9–10, 11, 17, 23–26, 27, 40–41, 49, 83, 106, 109, 122–123, 146; social media 17, 41; social resources 1–2, 23; social support 10, 122, 146
space 9, 11–14, 16–17, 23, 27, 36, 59, 67, 71, 78–80, 83–84, 91, 99, 104, 111, 117, 127, 129
spirituality 8, 18, 24–25, 27–28
stress 1–4, 6–8, 10–12, 14, 16, 18–19, 23–26, 30, 32–34, 40, 42, 44–45, 48, 50–57, 59, 60, 62, 64–67, 69, 70, 72, 74, 86, 89, 90, 92, 105–109, 116, 121–122, 125–128, 130, 132, 138–139, 146; acute stress 51–52; chronic stress 51–53, 57, 69, 126; psychological stress 3, 7, 51, 53, 89

WDEP 112–120
well-being 1–3, 5, 10–11, 16–17, 23, 25, 42, 48, 66, 121, 124, 126, 128, 134, 143, 146
wellness 7–8, 23–25, 28, 50, 58, 66, 120, 126, 130